ACCIDENT or ARSON?

Accident or Arson?

Bill Cosgrove

Rutledge Books, Inc. Danbury, CT

ALL RIGHTS RESERVED
Rutledge Books, Inc.
107 Mill Plain Road, Danbury, CT 06811
1-800-278-8533
www.rutledgebooks.com

Manufactured in the United States of America

Cataloging in Publication Data
Cosgrove, Bill
    Accident or Arson?

    ISBN: 1-58244-197-9

    1. Firefighters -- investigation -- Chicago. 2. Solving
crime. 3. Arson. 4. Accident.

Library of Congress Control Number: 2001098662

Dedication

This book is dedicated to the Chicago firefighters and paramedics who have sacrificed their lives while protecting the way of life we all enjoy in this great city of Chicago.

They will never be forgotten!

Acknowledgements

In the course of gathering all of the material for this book, I had the invaluable assistance of many people.

Captain Michael Deckelmann, William Kugelman, president of the Firefighters Union Local #2, Retired Fire Commissioner Raymond Orozco, and Gene Furmack of G&L Gifts for all his encouragement.

My brother, Mike Cosgrove, now retired Media Affairs Director, for all his knowledge of the Chicago Fire Department and the ambualance service.

My good friend, Phil Lamm, for the great photograph he supplied me with that ended up being the cover of this book.

Like my other book *The Noble Breed,* a very special thank you to Margaret (Peg) Campagna, who worked so hard to type this book. I will always be thankful...

To my good friend and boss, William C. Alletto, retired Deputy Fire Commissioner, without whom these stories would not have been possible.

My sincere appreciation to Chicago Fire Commissioner Jones T. Joyce for all his cooperation with this book.

As always, thank you to my lovely wife, Suzi, who always had the time to help me after a long day at work.

To my six children, and five grandchildren who encouraged me to write my third book.

Like my other books, contributions will be made to:

The Fireman's Annuity and Benefit Fund of Chicago, The Ende Menzer Walsh Retiree's, Widow's, and Children's Assistance Fund.

The Enemy

I AM MORE powerful than the combined armies of the world. I have destroyed more men, women and children than all the wars of all nations. I massacre thousands of people every year. I am more deadly than bullets, and I have wrecked more homes than the mightiest guns.

In the United States alone, I steal over 500 million dollars each year. I spare no one and I find my victims among the rich and poor alike; the young and old, the strong and weak. Widows know me to their everlasting sorrow. I loom up in such proportions that I cast my shadow over every field of labor.

I lurk in unseen places and do most of my work silently. You are warned against me, yet you heed me not. I am relentless, merciless, and cruel. I am everywhere, in the home, in the schools, in the factory, on land, in the air, and on the sea.

I bring sickness, degradation and death, yet few seek me out to destroy me. I crush, I maim, I devastate — I will give you nothing and rob you of all you have.

I AM YOUR WORST ENEMY
I AM RAMPANT FIRE.

Unknown Author

Most of the events in this story are true and actual accounts as they occurred. Some of the details and chronology have been altered to preserve anonymity.
Some of the names have been changed to protect the confidentiality of both the innocent and the guilty.
I have been granted a privilege, not through any special inspiration or insight, but through my everyday work.

I am a
"Firefighter"

Chapter 1

THE CLOCK RADIO GOES OFF AND ALL I HEARD WAS THE NEWS broadcaster's voice recapping last night's newsworthy events. The Chicago police have a suspect in custody for an apparent arson fire on Chicago's west side. An extra alarm fire took the lives of two elderly women and gutted a three-story building.

With my left hand, I press down the snooze button of the clock radio and fade back to sleep for another fast ten minutes. But only half asleep, I know there was another fire on the west side and somehow by the time I arrived at the firehouse, I would most likely be the fire marshal to relieve the fire marshal (investigator) on the third platoon, who was at the fire.

I sat up in my nice warm bed, and looked at the time. It was 05.32. I rubbed my eyes just enough to find my glasses and the clock radio clicks on again, and the broadcaster continues to talk about the Blackhawk's game last night. I shut it off. "That darn Gaelic Fire Brigade," I thought to myself. After a quick shower I got my first cup of coffee, and packed my bag for the firehouse. I am now in my Dodge van, making my way through the dark streets of my southwest neighborhood. Just like many other firefighters on the first platoon, we were going in!

I have a good heater in the van, and I will be warm by the time I get to the Dan Ryan Expressway. I thought to myself, I only have sixteen more payments left before it's mine!

WMAQ 670 radio broadcasts news and weather every ten minutes. The announcers said, "The weather today is going to be cloudy with possible snow flurries late this afternoon. Temperature in the low thirties and dropping down into the twenties tonight. The wind is out of the west at eight miles an hour."

I wondered if I had an extra pair of long johns in my locker, because the "hawk" would be out tonight. Traffic on the Ryan was heavy as usual, but there were no accidents reported, and I soon would be at Twenty-second Street, the Chinatown exit. The morning sky was beginning to lighten up to the east over Lake Michigan as I approached the firehouse.

The headquarters of the Office of Fire Investigation, OFI, is located at 1401 South Michigan, just south of Chicago's Loop. An old, tan-colored brick building, it has two red overhead doors facing west. In its early years, it was the home of Engine 104 and Hook and Ladder 31's quarters. The first floor was where we parked the three red and black marked fire department sedans that we used to respond to fires all across the city.

The rear of the first floor was where our offices were located. The second floor was where the bunkroom was located and also the lockers and showers for the firefighters (OFI fire marshals).

The Office of Fire Investigation is an integral part of the Chicago Fire Department, and is under the administrative control of the fire commissioner. The basic mission of the Office of Fire Investigation is the accurate documentation of events that came together to cause a fire or an explosion incident within Chicago's city limits.

As I walked through the backdoor of the firehouse, I thought to myself, "I am in my third year in OFI, and I never thought I would make one year." One fire marshal from the third platoon was sitting at one of four desks in a large room we called the "kitchen," which was also our office.

"Morning Mike, how's it going?" I asked.

He looked up at me and said, "Cos, we had seven fires yesterday. This is my second report of four, and Emmett is at a 2-11 on the West Side. He has his hands full-two dead and four injured."

"I know, it's the first thing I heard when the clock radio went off this morning," I said.

I poured a cup of hot coffee and walked over to a long counter along the south wall where the CFD portable radios were lined up in their chargers. "I'll call and see if he needs any help out there."

"Good," Mike said, "I'm sure he will be happy to hear from you, Cos."

I grabbed my radio, marked 463, and walked out onto the apparatus floor. All the fire gear was hanging along the south wall. My fire coat still had that acrid smell of smoke from the last day I worked. I threw my fire helmet, boots, and coat into the black and red sedan, also marked 463. With the portable radio in hand, I called Emmett McShane at the fire scene on the West Side.

"Four-six-three to 4-6-4 direct," I said, then waited. There was no answer. I repeated the call, and the radio crackled. Finally I heard, "Four-six-four to 4-6-3, go ahead!"

I said, "Hey, Marshal, you need some help out there?"

"You bet I do, Cos," he replied.

I said, "Don't leave the scene, I'm on my way."

"Message received, 4-6-4."

I picked up the "marshal line" which is the red phone for official fire department use only, and called the Main Fire Alarm

Office. I asked the dispatcher where the fire was located and he told me, "4301 West Adams, it's a 2-11 alarm."

I told the dispatcher 463 was responding to the fire to assist 464. "Okay, 4-6-3," the dispatcher said, "we will put you en route to the 2-11 fire at 4301 West Adams."

I said goodbye to Mike Deckelmann in the kitchen and pulled the red and black sedan out onto Michigan Avenue with my running lights on and siren going. Traveling west on the Eisenhower Expressway the traffic wasn't too bad because most of the rush hour traffic was eastbound at this time of the morning. I got off the Eisenhower at Pulaski and went north to Adams. You could see the smoke to the west. As I approached, the police had traffic blocked off. I parked the car out of the way of the working fire companies and started getting my fire gear on. Emmett McShane was standing outside of communications van 272. (All fire department vehicles have an identifying number.) As I walked over to him, he was getting some information from the police about where the suspect had been taken. He had been arrested and was brought to the Eleventh Police District at 3151 West Harrison Street.

Firefighters from Engine 95 and Truck 26 were still extinguishing small fires throughout the structure. Emmett McShane related to me that the still alarm of fire was at 0457 and upon the arrival of the Thirteenth Battalion, he called for a box alarm right away.

Fire was throughout the rear of the structure. As I walked around the back of the fire building, I could see the wooden rear staircase had been heavily consumed by fire.

Firefighters were overhauling what was left of that wooden staircase. There were electrical wires down on the ground that had fallen from the burning structure, and Com Ed was working in the alley.

It was not yet 0800, and I told Emmett I would take over. Firefighters were being relieved by the oncoming platoon. I called into my office and Captain Matt Moran answered. He said in a joking manner, "Marshal, where in the hell are you today?" I told him I had a lot of work out here and I would then go to Loretto Hospital to get the names of the injured. Matt Moran was my officer today, and he advised me that we had only two OFI cars in service because Carl Hopkins was in court all day.

"What's new, Marshal?" he said.

I replied, "I'll call you later." The Chicago Fire Department Photo Unit 492 was on the scene, and I told him that I wanted a lot of shots of the back of the structure because this fire had been determined by OFI to be of incendiary origin, and that it had been deliberately set. We would definitely be in court on this one, and I didn't want some asshole telling me later that we should have taken more photos. The burn patterns on the rear porch clearly indicated that this fire originated on the outside of the structure.

The firefighters of the Thirteenth Battalion, as always, did a great job holding this fire because it did not extend to the adjacent building to the west.

The interior of the structure had signs of heavy smoke and water damage in the front, but as I made my way through the hall toward the rear of the apartment, you could see very heavy fire destruction in the rear bedroom and kitchen areas.

The victims were found in the bedroom on the second floor, one on the bed and the other in the southwest corner of the room. Both were taken to the Cook County Morgue by the Chicago police.

Back outside on Adams Street, the fire companies were picking up the last of their fire hoses. Ice was everywhere, because it was cold out, about twenty degrees. The fire was extinguished, and the battle was over, but now the investigation of what caused the fire that took the lives of two women would continue. That had been my job for about three years.

I loved fighting fires, but I was always interested in how they originated. A few years after the firefighters strike against the city of Chicago, many of my fellow firefighters left the job because of attrition, retirements, and disabilities caused from fires and many rescue activities.

The strike left many scars and things were never the same again. Firemen moved to new firehouses, as I did. In the mid-eighties, one of my old friends, Bill Alletto, called me and asked if I would be interested in fire investigation. He said it would be hard work, not so much physical but mental, and a lot of report writing. I told him I didn't have much education, but he encouraged me and said most of the men joining the unit don't have college degrees, either. However, they could read blueprints, knew fire chemistry and building construction, had good average intelligence, and most of all, they had a lot of fire duty experience, and good common sense.

He also informed me that we would have to attend classes at the University of Illinois, Circle Campus. I thought to myself, what a great opportunity, but to return to school? I never did that well in school, but I knew my job as a firefighter. I had seniority in the fire department. I was honored that he had selected me for this new unit, but, as usual, I procrastinated. Another year went by and I tried to get into OFI, but there were no vacancies and you had to submit a resume. I had no idea how to make a resume, or as they say now, curriculum vitae. My wife, Suzi, helped and it turned out to be a pretty good resume.

Finally, after a long wait, Chief Alletto called me. He said he had one opening in the unit, and if I wanted to give it a try, there was a ninety-day detail. I had said I'd give it a try and the chief had responded, "It's not for everyone, but I think you will do well." This gave me some needed confidence, because I knew Bill Alletto had great insight for finding good people.

The first day I met with the chief, he tried not to overwhelm me with all the paperwork, but I was totally overwhelmed! I was a firefighter who needed help filling out a CFD Form 2 to make a trade with another firefighter, and writing detailed reports for a stickler like Chief Bill Alletto was somewhat intimidating! But my old boss had a calming effect on me, and was very encouraging. He was a firm believer that people from busy companies did well in these investigative positions. They were not afraid to work. Also, on my first day when I arrived at OFI, it seemed to be like an old reunion in Chief Alletto's office. One of our old captains from Engine 45, Larry Walsh, was sitting in a chair against the wall. He, too, was going to work in the Office of Fire Investigation. Larry had been laid up with the problem of diabetes. He had his time in on the job and surely could have retired. But no, not this guy. Larry loved being on the fire department and was one of the best fire officers I have ever worked with. Although he could not continue being a fire captain on a fire suppression company, Larry still wanted to remain in the fire service and was going to share his knowledge and experience of firefighting with the Office of Fire Investigation.

In order to respond to a fire and complete an investigation, you had to fill out a nineteen-page incident report by hand. You wouldn't believe the amount of information you needed to obtain at the fire scene in order to complete this form. Then another form went to the incident commander on the cause of the fire, and there was another form, structure cards, cross-index cards and the list of forms just goes on. Chief Alletto said that should a case reach the courts, this documentation was invaluable, and in his opinion, an absolute necessity.

We worked the same hours that all firefighters work, twenty-four hours on and forty-eight hours off. I was on the first platoon, and was assigned to a lieutenant who had six years less than I did on the fire department, and only one year in OFI. I asked myself, what the hell am I doing here?

The first fire I responded to was a 2-11 alarm fire on the West Side at 5533 West Washington Street. We reported to the chief of the Thirteenth Battalion, and he informed us that upon the arrival of Engine Company 96 and Hook and Ladder Company 29, there was a heavy smoke and fire condition on the first floor of the structure.

I had no idea what I was doing, so I helped an engine company with their hose line up to the second floor. The lieutenant I was working with told me not to help with fire extinguishing; we were "investigators." I told him in a few choice words that, first and always, I am a firefighter and I don't think we can investigate anything until this fire is extinguished. He went back into the fire car that we responded to this fire in, and I didn't see him for about an hour. In the meantime I helped extinguish the fire and also talked to the first-floor occupant. She related to me that she had been cooking on the kitchen stove, and she had stepped away for a minute to see something on television. Then she saw a large amount of smoke coming from the kitchen. She ran in to see what was burning, and there was fire on the cabinets and the ceiling. The firefighters of Engine Company 113 told me most of the fire was in the kitchen, and fire was blowing out the west window on the first floor. After the fire was extinguished, I returned to the first-floor kitchen. Sure enough, the gas stove burners were all in the "on" position. I wasn't sure what I was doing, but the kitchen area was completely burned-out, and the fire had burned through to the second and third floor. I kept thinking about what the OFI lieutenant had told me, and it really got my goat. What the fuck did he think he was, some prima donna? If Alletto had heard that remark, he would have gone through the ceiling.

You could see by the faces of the firefighters that they were just in one hell of a battle: blackened faces of soot, wet from sweat and the steam of the fire. They were backing the hose out of the burned-out first-floor apartment. I finally found my lieutenant, back in the fire car. I told him that I found out that the woman who lived on the first floor was cooking on the kitchen stove. He returned with me to the burned-out structure, and I showed him what I found. He said good job, and made a determination that the flames from kitchen stove burners had caused the fire.

While we were returning to our quarters I thought to myself, that wasn't so hard. As a matter of fact, I kind of enjoyed figuring out what had happened. But then, once we got back to OFI headquarters, I had to start the report. I think it took me about six hours to complete it! Matt Moran was our captain in the Office of Fire Investigation and he helped me out with the incident report, but he could only show me the steps to filling out the report, and said "Marshal, you have to learn to complete a fire report by yourself." In the Office of Fire Investigation you were called fire marshal, and not firefighter anymore. Well, it will take some getting used to, I said to myself. But Captain Moran loved to stroke us with the term "marshal." He was a funny, but a very sharp and capable fellow who worked with Chief Alletto and me in the old Sixteenth Battalion.

The Office of Fire Investigation had a day group with three senior fire marshals who had the responsibility to investigate major incidents, and to follow up the fires that were classified as "cause unknown or undetermined" by the twenty-four hour group.

Also on the day shift were Chief Alletto, the director of OFI, and Captain Pat Burns, the assistant director. The only female who worked in the OFI was our secretary, Margaret "Peggy" Campagna, who deciphered our handwritten reports, and typed them out for us.

I have been a firefighter for over fifteen years now, and one thing that I know for sure is that there are a lot of fires in Chicago. Before this unit was in service, most of the fires that occurred in Chicago were classified as undetermined in origin, and there wasn't any effort being put forth to find out the causes. This was because fire chiefs had to concentrate their efforts entirely on fire-fighting and did not have the time to determine the cause of the fire, or the value of a thorough fire investigation for cause.

To receive a fire call in OFI was different than when I was on a fire company, where the speaker opened and a dispatcher made a loud announcement to the fire companies. The address, and then the bell, would sound throughout the firehouse. In the Office of Fire Investigation, the red phone (the marshal line) would ring, and the dispatcher from the Fire Alarm Office would then say, for instance, that Battalion Nine is requesting OFI at his fire scene. Then the fire marshal who answered the phone would take the address of the fire and inform the dispatcher about which OFI car would be responding. This was different-there were no bells, you just reported whoever was up for the run, the address, what battalion requested OFI, and that was it.

OFI responded to all still and box alarm fires automatically in Chicago, from the northwest corner of the city, which is where Chicago O'Hare International Airport is located, to the southeast corner of the city where Wolf Lake meets the Indiana state border.

A still alarm is when there is a report of a fire and that is the initial call of a fire. The Fire Alarm Office dispatches two engine companies, two truck companies, and one battalion chief to the scene. Upon their arrival on the scene, the first fire company will report that they have a working fire. If this fire is more than the still alarm companies can handle, then they will request a "box." The Fire Alarm Office will then dispatch three more engine companies, one more truck company, a squad company, a command van for communications, one ambulance company, two more battalion chiefs, one OFI fire marshal, and the incident commander will be a deputy district chief. Now there are some fifteen pieces of equipment and some fifty-two people at the scene, and that is what is known as a still and box alarm.

Fires progressed by the numerical number eleven and I'm not sure why, but I believe that a "box" was struck, and the call was for a 2-11 alarm. Then there were eleven pieces of equipment dispatched to the fire scene. Fires continue to progress 2-11, 3-11, 4-11, 5-11, and then special alarms. I think this was one of the only things that did not change after the strike. Most of the Chicago Fire Department changed, and we all started to change, from firefighters to chiefs. The fire department had a rich tradition, a great camaraderie, and this also began to erode, which would not portend well for this great department!

The city changed and we signed contracts between the union and the city. The Chicago Fire Department was restructured from seven divisions to seven districts, and the twenty-five old battalions into twenty-four completely new battalions, all in different firehouses. Mayor Byrne appointed William Blair from Los Angeles, California, as fire commissioner. Even the union changed. After two successive and successful terms in the Office of the President of Local 2, Martin O. Holland succeeded Frank Muscare.

Marty Holland brought some harmony back to the fire department and Local 2. Times were still very rough, and because of so many changes, there were people who did not trust others, mainly in the upper echelon of the fire department. Marty Holland stayed focused, as we wanted our contract meticulously enforced. We also wanted respect for all Locals 2 members. Our executive board had demonstrated unified leadership, not only to our membership, but also to the city of Chicago.

One of the biggest changes in Chicago's history was when Jane Byrne lost the primary election in 1983. Chicago elected its first black mayor, Harold Washington, on April 15, 1983. It was the beginning of the Council Wars. Washington's voting allies versus "Vrdolyak's 29." Mayor Washington appointed a new fire commissioner, Louis Galante. He was one of our own from the West Side of Chicago, a damned good firefighter, and a highly intelligent individual.

Although city hall was in an uproar and nothing was being accomplished, the fire department was enjoying the benefits of our contract. The firefighters were making decent wages, we were working overtime, and working our "Daley days." We had self-contained breathing apparatus for each firefighter, five men on all the rigs, and portable radios for more effective communications on the fire ground.

In the early afternoon of November 25, 1987, Mayor Washington died of a heart attack in his office. They say he died of a massive cardiac arrest, and was found slumped over his desk.

Mayor Washington had been good to the firefighters, giving us one of our best contracts. He knew how firefighters put their lives on the line day in and day out for the citizens of Chicago.

The mayor's death left the city of Chicago in political confusion. Less than an hour after Mayor Washington's funeral, the politicians began to decide who would succeed Washington. They started meetings behind closed doors, using all their powers.

The backroom meetings were held about who was going to run Chicago, and how long that person would be in office. Would an acting mayor serve until the next regularly scheduled mayoral election in 1991, or until the next scheduled municipal election in 1989? After much controversy, on December 2, 1987, Eugene Sawyer was declared acting mayor of Chicago.

I started in the school system in order to learn how to become a fire investigator. The first school I attended was at the Robert J. Quinn Fire Academy. The course was Fire Causes and Arson Investigation. The class was on Tuesday night from 1830 to 2130 and guess who my teacher was? That's right, Chief William Alletto-what a coincidence!

Bill Alletto was not only my friend, but he was one of the first officers I had worked with on the fire department. After some fifteen years, here he is my boss again, and my teacher, and what a great teacher! He knew his job as a firefighter and fire boss, and was internationally recognized as an authority on fire/arson investigation.

After school, Alletto and I would go to Stages Restaurant at Thirty-first and Union. Chief Alletto told me about the arson fire at 2847 North Milwaukee where three brave Chicago firefighters lost their lives. I went to the funeral, as I have gone to almost all the funerals of fallen firefighters. I think that when one of our own is taken away from us while performing his duties, we all have to stop what we are doing, return to our lockers, get our class A costumes, and attend our fallen comrade's funeral.

I remember standing at attention on Michigan Avenue and Delaware Street in front of Holy Name Cathedral. Shoulder to shoulder, dressed in our class A uniforms, we awaited the Chicago Fire Department pumpers. In the distance you could hear the almost crying, mournful sounds of the bagpipes, as we watched in silence. As the three pumpers came to rest in front of

The Funeral of Our Fallen Comrades

me, I thought "three again." Why are they in threes? One by one, the three flag-draped caskets were ever so gently lifted and, with a very loud, "Detail, attention!" firefighters from all over our nation lined the street, and snapped to attention. After a slight pause, the command "Detail, salute!" was given, and the white-gloved hands of thousands of firefighters rose to salute these brave men.

Why is it always cold out when we attend the funerals, I asked myself, standing at attention. "Truss roof" is why we are standing here. It is a widow-maker. It is a fact that firefighters have to ventilate a burning structure to release the hot gases that collect in the roof area. There is only one way to ventilate this type of structure: open the roof.

I thought about the fire and Captain Nockels, a twenty-nine-year veteran, and the two young boys, Michael Forchione who was killed on his birthday, and Michael Talley, twenty-six years old with just three years on the job. They were doing their job, Bill Alletto continued in his remarks, but what they weren't aware of at the time, was that there was an inferno below them that structurally compromised the roof.

They said the fire was arson! A deliberately set fire for profit. That's when I knew I wanted to get into OFI. I told Bill Alletto that if there was a way I could learn how to catch a dirty lowlife motherfucker who sets a fire, then I want to learn about fire investigation. Alletto nodded and smiled, saying confidently, "You will be good at it."

This is what I learned about this fire that took the lives of these three brave and noble men.

It was just another day in the firehouse at 4911 West Belmont, but in a way it was going to be a special day. Mike Forchione was just twenty-nine years old today. They would have cake and cof-fee later. Mike Talley was celebrating his third anniversary on the job. Engine 7 and Hook and Ladder 58 and Ambulance 7 are just like many firehouses across this city. But on February 1, 1985, not far from Engine 7 and Hook and Ladder 58's firehouse, at about 0300, two Korean men were setting a fire to an electronics company, a television and stereo shop located at 2847 North Milwaukee Avenue.

Michael Talley had just finished his watch when the still alarm came in: "2847 North Milwaukee for everybody!" It was cold outside-the temperature was minus nine degrees and the wind was out of the northeast at ten miles per hour. The wind chill factor was twenty degrees below zero!

"We got a hit, boys" Captain Nockels said. Truck 58 was the second truck on the scene of the extra alarm fire, and was ordered to the rear and to open the roof! Ladders were thrown in the rear of the structure. Heavy smoke conditions were fanned by the wind. At around 0402, the roof of the burning structure suddenly collapsed. Three of the men, Captain Nockels, and Firefighters Forchione and Talley disappeared, plunging with the roof into the fire. A 3-11 alarm was pulled on the fire and the fire department went into a rescue mode.

Two of the bodies were found soon after the fire was under control, but the third firefighter was not recovered for some seven hours.

The police had the owner of the building in the back seat, asking this Korean motherfucker what could burn in the store, because it looked "suspicious." The Korean was very nervous and said he didn't want this to happen. He said he had hired a man to set fire to the structure. Chicago police detectives were questioning both of those men at Grand Central Area Police Headquarters, and Assistant States Attorney Jeff Wernick got signed confessions from both of them.

What I learned from Bill Alletto was there are ways that

when investigative procedures are carefully followed, we can catch the arsonist who is responsible for causing deaths of both firefighters and civilians.

One of the first things you need to know in fire investigations is a little bit of law, mainly the law of arson and how it pertains to the fire department and the courts. There were pertinent state statutes we needed to know as they related to arson, and Bill Alletto knew the law of arson as well or better than most lawyers. During the cause determination part of the class, Alletto gives a fairly effective rule of thumb guide for determining the origin and the cause of the fire. This was a sixteen-week class and was part of the City College Fire Science Degree program. I got three hours of college credit and did very well in the class and final exam.

But the most important part about this investigation work was the fact that we were responding to fires throughout Chicago, learning firsthand about cause and origin by actually being at the fire. Working with Bill Alletto and Matt Moran gave me a new outlook on the fire department. There haven't been real good days since the strike, but we did remind each other of the "good old days."

Chapter 2

MATTHEW MORAN WAS THE CAPTAIN OF THE OFFICE OF FIRE Investigation. A great man whom I had worked with many times before. Matt was the engineer of Engine 61, lieutenant of Hook and Ladder 15, and the captain of Engine 30.

Matt worked five days a week in OFI and was in charge of the men who worked the twenty-four-hour platoon. He gave out the assignments to the fire marshals on a daily basis. He enjoyed calling us "marshals," although he told us that we were fire-fighters first, and then we were marshals who investigated fires, and never to forget that!

Matt had an excellent working knowledge of building construction and because of working in a high incident fire area, he had the opportunity to observe the phenomena of fire behaving in all of its complex eccentricities. He had good working knowledge of electricity and how code violations play a role in fires. But the most important part of Captain Moran was his great sense of humor. He could help you out of the worst situations with a lot of class and knowledge, and always made you feel good with a little humor. He really knew how to handle men and was an excellent supervisor.

The work was hard in OFI because there was so much to

learn. We were busy. Total runs averaged out to about 160 to 200 investigations per month. This may not sound like much, but each fire incident we responded to, was three hours of paperwork for me when we returned to our quarters! Most days there was no sleep, and we ran two or sometimes three OFI cars for the twenty-four hours.

The cars were two 1978 Suburbans, the old battalion chief's buggies, and one black and red Ford sedan. I don't remember what year it was, but most of the time it was in the shop for repairs. Sometimes the siren would work and sometimes it would not, and that was the way it was on most of the vehicles. They were junk and there is nothing else I can say about it. They were shop junks. Matt used to kid around and would say, "The new cars will be here next week," but they never came.

What did come were fires. Once the battalion chiefs found out that we were there to assist them, they began to rely heavily on us. We automatically responded on all still and boxes citywide, fatalities caused by fire, all multiple injuries because of fire, all extra alarms, and any structural fire or explosion incident as required.

The red phone rang on the desk in the kitchen. I picked it up and said, "OFI, Cosgrove."

"This is the Main Fire Alarm Office, Cos. We have a fire. Battalion Six is requesting OFI at 1420 North Maplewood." I wrote the time, 1418, and the address in my note pad.

I told the dispatcher that 463 was taking the fire at 1420 North Maplewood. It was imperative because of the U.S. Supreme Court decision of Michigan v. Tyler that an immediate response be effected to all requests for investigations, and that on arrival, we let the Fire Alarm Office know we were on the scene. The fire was only a few blocks west of Western Avenue, and south of North Avenue. I was learning how to respond better by knowing the streets. As I arrived on the scene, I met with Sixth Battalion Chief Montgomery and he informed me that there was a heavy volume of smoke billowing from the windows on the first floor on the north side of the building, and fire was issuing from the window in the center on the west side of the structure.

"Okay, Chief, I'm going to take a look inside the building." He told me they were not done putting out the fire yet. I told him it's okay, I will be all right. Inside the first floor, there was more junk than a person could collect in a lifetime. As I climbed over all the junk there was the added challenge of smoke and heat in my face. I was too far in to turn around, so I just bit the bullet and continued in to where Engine 57 had their line. They were all standing around in this burned-out smoking room, looking at me as I almost fell on my ass. As I jumped down from the piles of paper, books, and other shit this guy had accumulated, one of the firemen joked, "You should've come through the back. It would've been a lot easier."

"Hey, does anyone live here?" I asked.

"No, it's abandoned," the officer of Engine 44 said. "Once the guy couldn't move around anymore he just said fuck it, and left. My name is Dennis Sobieski . . . the place was wide open when we got here. There was fire blowing out this window over here. This room looks to be a dining room."

I had just learned about fire load which refers to the amount of combustibles and the weight per square foot. There's enough paper and shit to support an extra alarm, I thought to myself.

The firemen continued washing down the two rooms on the first floor that were burning. I walked out the backdoor and onto the wooden rear porch of this abandoned three-story brick building. As I walked around the outside of the building looking for evidence of arson, this was not the first fire for this joint I said to myself. I checked in with the Chicago police officer who was assigned to this scene. We exchanged a little information. There was an elderly woman standing on her front porch across the street from the fire building, and I knew I wanted to talk to her. The interview disclosed that she knew what time the fire occurred, and who called the CFD.

The old woman invited me into her home. She informed me that there had been "a lot of drug traffic in and out of there," meaning the fire building, and she said further, "We were all scared that something was going to happen, and it did!" She said this was the second fire this week, and there had been a shooting over the weekend. I went back inside and saw the firemen picking up their hose lines. I talked with the chief and told him that it was a deliberately set fire, and that I would call for the Bomb and Arson Unit, to initiate a criminal investigation of this incendiary fire incident.

The origin of the fire was in the first floor in what appeared to be a dining room, along the outside wall. The cause was persons unknown igniting rubbish with an open flame in this abandoned vacant building.

The Sixth Battalion reported to the Main Fire Alarm Office that we were all in service and returning to quarters. I liked abandoned buildings because you can fill out a vacant building report a lot faster than a full incident report.

The Office of Fire Investigation was beginning to become very popular, and by January 1, 1988 there were thirty-five people working at 1401 South Michigan Avenue. There were always people going to a new school to take one of the many classes associated with fire investigation. Chief Alletto was in his glory; this was his dream to have enough investigators to investigate all the fires that occurred in Chicago. Two investigators for each fire scene, because like any other job on the Chicago Fire Department, there is a lot of danger being left at a fire scene when all the fire companies have returned to their quarters. It is just better with two guys and you can do a better job, looking out for one another's safety as the investigation is conducted.

We had free rein of who would be partners with each other on the first shift. I worked most of the time with Jack Lumsden or Tony Maritato.

Jack had been in OFI the longest and was, to me, about the best marshal in the unit. He was thorough about everything from whatever OFI car we responded with, to the simple fire scene. He was one of those guys who dotted all of his i's and crossed all of his t's. I never had the opportunity to work as a firefighter with him, but I am very sure he was a good fireman.

Then there was Tony. He came into the unit a little after me, but he was the total opposite of Jack. Tony was fun, and he didn't take anything seriously. He was a firefighter on the North Side of the city on a busy Hook and Ladder, Truck Company 47. He had seen a lot of fire duty and took everything with a grain of salt. But when he had to be serious, he certainly could be!

In the morning, Matt liked to sit us down and tell us about arson, although he didn't liked to use the word "arson." He said, "We investigate fires. The police take care of arson after we determine that the fire is incendiary, and their criminal investigation indicates a criminally set fire. Some things you guys should watch for when you're making investigations is that restaurants and bars seldom burn when they are open. Invariably, they burn between 2 A.M. and 5 A.M. For some reason, businesses that are losing money burn a lot more often than businesses that are making money. Just remember, before this unit was in service, about half the fires were classified as accidental or cause unknown, and because of this, many deliberately set fires were not investigated. For us fellas, we should never look for arson. We must always look for the cause of the fire, and document our conclusions." This was one of the first things Chief Alletto taught us.

"So here's a little arson trivia, men! The first American law relating to arson was enacted in Maryland in 1638. It decreed: 'Malicious trespasses as to burn or destroy willfully a house or a stack of corn is a felony.' Penalties required the offender to suffer the pain of death by hanging. However, a less severe penalty was permitted. The offender could lose his hand or be burned on the forehead with a hot iron. That's the way we should deal with arson."

Every morning, Matt would humor us with stories, but in all, he was always teaching us about fire investigation. It was easy and fun to learn from this fine man.

Each morning in OFI, in all firehouses across this city, we completed an inspection of our rig and a basic checklist of all the tools and the equipment that we carry.

In the cold winter months in Chicago, you dress warmly in layered clothing that can be removed so you remain comfortable. Don't get frostbite: keep all your extremities, hands and feet, protected because you could be out all night.

We were sitting back watching the television in the firehouse when I heard on the radio, "Engine 35 on the scene, 1737 North Campbell. We got smoke showing."

I looked up at the big clock on the wall, it was 1950. I was working with Lieutenant Carlos Mosqueda because I was still training. I knew we were up for the next fire, so I took the portable radio and set it on the table next to me.

There was silence, but the television was still loud enough although I didn't care what was on the screen. "Battalion Six to Main, we have a two-story frame 25 by 50, occupied, fire on the second floor. All companies are working."

I looked over at Carlos. He was completely absorbed in the

television, but I knew that firefighters were leading out lines, and raising the main to the roof. My adrenaline started up. I just could not sit at this kitchen knowing that firefighters were out there in the cold working as hard as they could to stop this fire. Then, "Battalion Six to Main, send in OFI," and the red phone started to ring. I picked it up. "OFI, Cosgrove," I said.

Mike Berry in the office said, "Cos, Battalion Six is requesting an OFI car at his fire at 1737 North Campbell. I told him that 465 was responding."

"Carlos, we have a fire," I said as I took the radio and my notebook off the table and walked out onto the cold apparatus floor where the cars were parked. I started the car and Bob Villanueva said, "I'll get the door, Cos." Carlos jumped into the passenger seat and, with the lights flashing, we pulled out onto Michigan Avenue.

Traffic was light and we were on the scene in about ten minutes. I put my gear on while looking at the building. There was only a small amount of smoke emanating from the second-floor windows, but a lot of steam.

We reported to the Sixth Battalion Chief Montgomery and he informed us that upon his arrival on the scene, fire was issuing out the window on the second floor in the back of the building. The chief told us that the gas was shut off to the second floor.

Carlos told me he was going to get the Chicago police R.D. number, and see if the officer knew anything about the fire. He liked talking to the police because before he was a fireman, he was on the Chicago Police Department.

I looked at him and said, "Okay, Lou," and pulled my hip boots up and went straight up to the second floor. The firefighters were overhauling the remains of what was left of a bedroom. I asked the firemen what was burning when they arrived.

"When we got up here, the pipe man on Engine 35 said the whole thing was on fire, and there was this loud roaring noise that was here also. I think it was coming out of this heater." He was pointing down to a portable space heater called a "salamander."

The smoke cleared, and the firefighters finished washing down the burned-out rooms on the second floor. As they pulled their hoses down, I was left in a cold, dark room to try to figure out what happened there.

There was heavy charring throughout the rear of this apartment, but it was very heavy around the doorway leading into a bedroom. The ceiling was down and there was a hole in the roof above the burned-out bedroom. I thought to myself, good place to open the roof, because I was a truck man and I knew about roofs.

I returned to the ground floor to find Carlos. He was in the building next door with the police officer. Chief Montgomery said they were all picked up and were returning to quarters. We exchanged some names and numbers and the chief asked me to call him when we found a cause. Then engine, truck, and the chief left the scene.

I went into the building next to the fire building. There were about twenty people sitting and standing. Children wrapped in blankets with a worried look on their faces. Carlos and the police officer were in the kitchen.

As I entered the kitchen, Carlos and the police officer were interviewing the occupant of the burned-out apartment. The occupant spoke Spanish, and they were not getting very far because they did not speak Spanish.

We got a young boy of about twelve to interpret. The gas had been turned off and the father had brought two portable kerosene heaters from his work to heat the apartment. When the door in the bedroom had been closed, the heater was directly in front of the door. The man said when he discovered the fire, the door was burning.

I returned to the second floor of the burned apartment. You could see a round mark on the bedroom door where the heat was blowing out of the salamander. I showed Carlos the heater and the point of origin. We examined the rest of the structure and completed the investigation after ten-thirty and then returned to the firehouse.

The determination of the cause of this fire was the result of the improper placement of a portable heater. The fire was classified as accidental, and no further investigation was required by the fire department.

On our way back, Carlos said, "How about stopping for something to eat?" I wasn't that hungry, but I knew Carlos was, because he hadn't had any pizza with Jack, Tony, and me at seven. This is one of the bad drawbacks about OFI. There was no food club; it just never worked. At one time Tony Maritato tried to make a cooking club, but one of the cars was always out at a fire. Many times after cooking a big dinner we ended up just making sandwiches out of the meat.

Later, Jack Lumsden took over as house treasurer. He bought coffee, tea, hot chocolate, and some soup. But as far as eating well, you just were on your own.

We stopped at a greasy all-night grill on Roosevelt Road and Canal Street. You could smell the onions a mile away and the burgers weren't bad, but at 2300, I knew digestion was going to be a problem for me, so I stayed in the car.

As I sat outside of the all-night grill waiting for Carlos, the radio was blaring again and Engine 63 reported on the scene with smoke showing. Just minutes later I heard "Battalion Seventeen to Englewood." It was the voice of Chief Caponera. "We have a three-story brick building about 75 by 100, occupied with fire on the rear porches of the second and third floors."

I looked back into the grill to see how Carlos was making out with his hamburger and he was into a full conversation with a Chicago policeman.

As I stared down the street, steam was rising from the manhole covers on Canal. It was cold out and firefighters were going to work. The radio crackled again, and in a clear voice you could hear, "Battalion Seventeen to Englewood, give us a box." I listened for the address, and the office announced a still and box alarm at 6523 South Maryland. Carlos opened the door and got in.

"What's going on?" he said.

I replied, "Engine 63 just caught a fire on Sixty-fifth and Maryland, and the Seventeenth Battalion boxed it."

Carlos said, "That's Jack and Tony's fire, right?"

I said, "Yeah, but we're back up for the next fire."

We returned to 1401 South Michigan. The house was empty. Carlos went to eat his hamburger and I started sorting through my field notes in order to start our report.

I told Carlos I would write the report, and he could fill out the journals. I liked doing it this way. Some of the marshals liked to take half the report for themselves and give their partner the other half. But when Chief Alletto read the report, if something was wrong, I didn't want to get my ass chewed out for something the other guy had written in the report.

Carlos finished the journals, and all the attachments that go with the report, and then went to bed.

The fire on Maryland was "struck out," but I knew it would be some time before Jack and Tony returned.

When I finished the fire report from our fire up on North Campbell, it was a little past three in the morning. I slowly went up the steel winding staircase that led up to the locker room on the second floor. The firehouse was freezing. There were only two radiators in the bunkroom. There were about twelve beds in the bunkroom and no one but me and Carlos, and he was in the front, in the officers' room.

I used a sleeping blanket, because it was so cold. There was a large wooden table in the center of the bunkroom with a red marshal line on it. That is how we received a fire call. There were no watches like in other houses. You went to bed and when the marshal line rang, you answered. I don't remember if I fell asleep or just dozed off when the marshal line rang. It was the Main Fire Alarm Office. Battalion Twenty-one was requesting OFI at his fire.

I repeated the address, "11422 South Maplewood" back to the office, and told him 465 was responding. I woke Carlos and went downstairs. Tony and Jack were working on their report. I looked at the clock. It was 0505. I said, "See ya tomorrow, men," and grabbed the portable radio. The fire was only an alley garage fire, but all fires, regardless of whether the fire is accidental or of incendiary origin, should be investigated and documented in order to prevent similar occurrences, especially where patterns develop or similarities are observed. We could have a firebug on our hands.

One big change that the fire department started was the first responder. Today, firefighters do a lot more than fight fires. In the case where all ambulances are committed, engine companies and truck companies become first responders, and are oftentimes a patient's only hope between life and death.

Now, regardless of the situation, the firefighters are the care providers for victims at accident scenes. I am sure there is going to be a lot of training in the next few years in basic and advanced life support techniques.

Firefighters, most of the ones that I know, are not going to be very happy with this "First Responder" program. When they took this job, they never thought of being an "ambulance guy." The great Andy Kowalski, who worked with Bill Alletto on Snorkel 3, called them "paragorics."

But, hey, we have to face the facts-the job is not just about fires anymore. In most cities around this country firefighters are involved in programs just like this First Responder. Firefighters are highly stressed everyday, and yet we sit around for many hours waiting for the next fire alarm. Now, these emergency medical calls push the stress level higher because of the unpredictable medical call that we must face.

A perfect example of this was on April 23, 1984, a virus was identified that could be very dangerous to firefighters and paramedics. It is called AIDS (acquired immune deficiency syndrome). We must be very careful out there, very careful. This virus will kill you before you know why or how it happened.

Firefighters are not subject to this deadly disease like the paramedics are. The paramedic is out there responding to incidents every day and many of their victims have this disease and there is protection for you, but you have to be careful.

A recent study came out with remarkable figures in January. Fire deaths have fallen to a new low, 23 percent lower than eight years ago. They say the major factor in this low percentage is because of the use of smoke detectors. Well I do agree about smoke detectors, but there are many other factors that this study forgot to mention.

I believe the main factor is that we have firefighters. Five on every rig in the city. When we respond to fires, every firefighter has his own "mask," a self-contained breathing apparatus which allows him or her to get deeper into a fire. Both the rescue of lives and the extinguishing of fires are affected by firefighters with a mask.

Another factor is fast water lead outs, or a very good method of sequence of laying hose from the engine to the fire.

Fire prevention has improved with inspections of code violations. Fire investigations must also be factored in, because the fire investigation is the basis for efficient fire prevention. It is only by accurate fire cause determination that knowledge is obtained that can be used to prevent incidents from occurring again.

Chief Alletto has developed a highly structured and formalized unit with OFI, which includes testing. I have been in school for a few months, but I have learned a lot about fires, and fire investigation. I have investigated over thirty fires so far, but every one has been sent back by Alletto with red corrections on every page of the report. He used this method as a teaching tool, to make us more proficient and professional, and so our reports could stand legal scrutiny.

We listened to radios all day long in OFI, so we knew ahead of time that a chief was requesting whatever OFI marshal was up for the run. Therefore, we all were aware.

As the day passed, fires were occurring across the city. Two of the fires requested OFI and we were up next. Waiting and knowing that if a box is pulled, you are going. It did not take long.

Engine 95 and 17, Trucks 26 and 14, and Squad 2 responded to a still alarm fire located at 851 North Kedvale shortly after 2100 hours in early March.

Upon their arrival on the scene, they reported a working fire, and Chief Gawenda called for OFI. When I arrived on the scene, the fire was almost totally extinguished. Chief Gawenda was in the Thirteenth Battalion that day. He informed me that fire was venting from the basement window on the east side and heavy black smoke was emanating from the windows in the attic front and rear. He further stated that some trouble had broken out between the owner and some man who is now down the corner. A woman said that he had started the fire. "Shit," I said to myself. I hate it when someone is having trouble. It is harder to get information from everyone around, because no one will say anything.

"Thanks, Chief, I think I will take a look." I followed the hose lines around the back of the structure as they led down a rear stairway into a basement.

I stopped for a second to look up at firefighters standing in the doorway off a small back porch. Pike poles in hand just waiting for the chief to tell them to "pick up."

I made my way down the stairs into the basement. Flashlights with their strong beams probed the burned floor above them, looking for signs of smoke. As my boots splashed through the high water in the basement, someone yelled to me, "Are you the arson guy?"

I said, "Yeah, you know, from OFI," with a laugh.

"I'm the captain of Engine 77," he said. "I think you got some arson here."

I asked him why he thought that. He said this bedroom smelled like gasoline. It sure did. I lifted a small part of a mattress in this center bedroom, and the odor hit me head on. There was certainly an odor similar in smell to gasoline.

The companies started to pick up. I returned to the front of the house, and interviewed the owner. She said she was having problems with the occupant of the basement apartment. "He is behind in his rent, and he is causing trouble, so I evicted him."

Now two other ladies came up and told me they had heard Kevin say, "If we can't live here, then I am going to burn the place down." I took my portable radio out of my pocket and, looking down the street, saw the firefighters bedding the rest of their hose. I called the Main Fire Alarm Office and requested that the

Chicago Police Bomb and Arson section respond to this incident immediately.

I returned into the first floor of the burned structure. There were no lights as I walked toward the back or the kitchen area. The fire had escalated in intensity to cause this much damage in such a short time. I went back into the basement. I checked the heating unit, and ruled it out as a cause. Then the hot water tank, and the electrical system. Chief Alletto always said that fire investigation is a process of elimination. The worst fire damage was in a center bedroom that was kind of makeshift or just thrown together. There was an odor similar in smell to that of gasoline. That's how it looks on paper. But it smells like gas and I know for sure you can't or shouldn't have gasoline inside a bedroom of a single family dwelling!

All the fire engines are now gone, and there is still a crowd of people out in front of the house. I still have to interview this woman named Annie. She is the person who heard this guy Kevin say he would burn this place down. Every time I tried to talk, this black guy named Raymond would start calling Annie a liar, saying, "She don't know what she's talking about."

Where is Bomb and Arson? I called over a half hour ago! I walked over to the beat cop and said, "How long before B and A will get here?"

The beat officer said to me, "I will have to call them when you make a determination."

I said to him, "I called for a B and A car a half hour ago."

He just looked at me and said, "They don't respond until I call. That's the rule."

I said, "You are fucking with me, aren't you?" The beat cop said no.

"I have a fucking arson fire, with physical evidence, and a witness that will identify the arsonist!" I yelled.

He said, "Do you want me to call them?"

I said "Yes, get on your fucking radio and call!"

Then he said to me, "I have to call them on a Bell phone line over at the Seven-Eleven store."

I returned to take the information from the owner, but I find out another fight is going on. Well that's just about enough for me, and I got into the red and black sedan and left that scene in a hurry. I can't believe I had an arson fire with a suspect, and the police did not want anything to do with all this evidence. Well, I am really pissed about it!

All the way back to the firehouse I could not take my mind off of what just happened back on Kedvale Ave. I returned just after midnight. The other cars were out, and I listened to the radios along the south wall of our kitchen/office. I made a pot of fresh coffee, and got my notes together from the fire. The first thing I am going to do is call over to the Bomb and Arson section to see if they have their heads stuck up their asses, I said to myself. What the fuck are they, prima donnas?!

With my coffee in hand, I dialed up Bomb and Arson and said good morning to Detective Ciolli. I introduced myself as Cos, in OFI, and told him I wanted to notify him of an arson fire.

"Oh, yeah, Cosgrove from the fire on Kedvale."

I said "Right."

He told me he had sent Detective Grano to the scene, and asked if I saw him there. I said, "No, because the citizens started getting out of control with no police, no firemen, and no gun, so I got the hell out of there"

"Where was the beat cop, Cos, while all of this was going on?"

I answered, "He was at the Seven-Eleven calling Bomb and Arson." I told Detective Ciolli I had an arson fire with gasoline poured onto a mattress on a bed. I also had two witnesses who heard the perpetrator say he was going to burn the building down. "Now what else do you want me to do?"

"Well, Cos," he says, "you know we can't go out on every run because you guys will have us all over the city. So the beat cop should check it out first, and if he sees that a crime has been committed he calls us." Ciolli continued, "You know, Cos, there are some guys in your unit [OFI] that think everything is arson, so you know we got to check it out first."

I said, "Detective Ciolli, it really doesn't matter to me if you guys come to my fire or not. So if I call again for your unit to respond and the beat car tells me they will be here in two hours, do you think I will stay at a fire scene for two hours? Let me tell you, I won't wait!"

I filled out the journals and some structure cards about the fire on Kedvale Avenue.

The radio crackled, "Four-six-three to Englewood. Would you notify Bomb and Arson about this incident." Jack Lumsden needs B and A, it's going to be a long night, and I was tired. At 0145 I made a decision not to do the report until morning, because when you're tired the report takes twice as long, and you could make mistakes. I went to bed.

The marshal line started to ring. I must have had a pretty good hold, because I didn't pick up on the first ring.

I answered "OFI, Cosgrove."

"Cos, Englewood Alarm Office, Battalion Eighteen is requesting an OFI car at his scene at 6748 South Halsted." Half-asleep, I repeated the address.

As I was getting dressed I was wondering who was in Battalion Eighteen. I was beginning to know the chiefs requesting OFI for investigations and I didn't remember the Eighteenth calling OFI. Then I descended down the long winding stairway from the second floor.

In the kitchen, Jack was working on his report. He said he heard Chief Foran call for OFI, but he didn't sound like it was a big incident because Chief Foran sent the second companies back to quarters.

Jack suggested using the Dan Ryan Expressway to Sixty-ninth Street, then west to Halsted. I took his advice. I went to the Dan Ryan. As I was responding, there wasn't much radio traffic. I thought to myself, if it was a fire you would hear a lot more on the radio. As I approached the scene, Engine 84 was on the corner, and there were many police cars around with their lights flashing.

I parked the car and walked over to the engine. One of the firefighters told me Chief Foran was looking for OFI, and he was in the alley. As I walked down to see Chief Foran, I could see a small crowd of police and firemen standing next to a dumpster. Chief Foran said, "Hey, Cos, the order says if you have a burn victim call OFI, and we have a burn victim," as he points down next to the dumpster.

I flashed my light over where the chief was pointing. A body was face down in the alley, most of the clothing was burned off, and the upper torso was badly blistered. The area was roped off, at both ends of the alley. Foran informed me that Ambulance 1 found the body, and it was burning. They called for a full still alarm. When Engine 84 arrived on the scene they, used a couple of hand pumps for extinction.

I talked to paramedics Chuck Peters and Bill O'Boyle on Ambulance 1, and they informed me they were given a run for an injured person in this alley. Once they saw the smoke, they jumped out of the rig and found a burning body behind the dumpster. The paramedics said, "So, Cos, we called for a full still."

"Thanks men," I said.

Two plainclothes detectives walked up to me and said, "Are you Cosgrove from OFI?"

"Am I under arrest?" I answered. "Yeah, I'm Cosgrove from OFI."

The detectives said, "We were told to watch out for you, because Detective Ciolli said you waited for us on Kedvale." I took a better look. "Bomb and Arson Dick's Detective Guest and Barzydlo," he said. "Sorry we missed you at the Kedvale fire. We got an arrest, did you know?"

I looked at him with wonder in my eyes. "For arson?" I asked.

"No, no, for disorderly conduct," and they smiled.

"So what do you know about this one, Cosgrove?" Detective Guest said.

"I am not a detective, but I think this may be a homicide, and robbery, with all his ID cards and wallet all over this alley."

"One thing I am not sure of, is why I am in this alley at five o'clock in the morning. I am supposed to find the origin and cause of a fire. I can see that the victim is the origin of the fire, and the cause was the result of an unknown person deliberately pouring a flammable liquid and igniting same with an open flame. May he rest in peace, and I am out of here, men."

Barzydlo yelled, "You don't want to know how we're going to investigate this fire?"

I said, "No, thank you!"

"I thought all you guys wanted to be detectives in OFI," he said.

"No, I am a firefighter and that is all I want to be. See ya, men."

I walked over to Chief Foran and at first, he thought it was funny getting me out for this. I told him I was going to call this a homicide in my report, if only I knew what type of report I was supposed to use. He laughed, and told the office that we were returning to our quarters.

While I was returning to OFI headquarters I thought about the young black man in the alley, but I also was thinking about how to word the report and what form I was supposed to use. It was 0700 and the second platoon was coming in, and so was the day shift, Matt and Tom Purdy.

I asked Peggy what form I should use for the homicide in the alley. She said "I think it's a special investigation form, but I will ask Matt." I said, "No, Peg. I want him to think I knew that." She said, "Okay."

I was two reports behind, and I knew I wasn't staying here in this firehouse to finish writing them. There was no overtime for reports then. What I needed was to get sleep first, and I went home.

I got the rest I needed, but I still had two reports to write by my next workday. It was very difficult to try to learn about fire investigation, go to school, and make time for my family.

Chapter 3

THE NEXT DAY AT THE FIREHOUSE, I WAS INTRODUCED TO TWO SPECIAL agents from the Bureau of Alcohol, Tobacco, and Firearms (ATF), John Maroca and John Malooly. They were going to ride with us in OFI and assist in the investigations of fires. It was a program that the Chicago Fire Department and the Department of the Treasury had come up with to train the agents.

Eugene Sawyer Jr. was now the acting mayor of Chicago. Local 2 union president, Martin O. Holland, was wasting no time negotiating a new contract with the city. Together with the executive board members, they were discussing issues and making recommendations for a four-year contract that would benefit the firefighters and paramedics. Some of the issues were wages, job rights, furlough selections, and trades of Daley days. Fire Commissioner Lewis Galante, who was a firefighter who had come up through the ranks, knew we should get a good contract and was personally involved with these negotiations.

Chief Alletto was on ATF's National Response Team (NRT). The NRT was to help and assist local fire departments with any significant arson and explosive incidents that they were requested to respond to. Frank Hart was ATF's supervisor of the Arson

Task Force in Chicago. Between Chief Alletto and Frank Hart, they came up with this "ride along" program.

Firemen are not usually receptive to new programs, and this was no exception. I wasn't up for the run, so I got my rig, checked out, and started writing the two reports from the last day. They are always due. You can be late with a report, but not too late!

It didn't take long before the first still and box alarm came in that morning. It was somewhere on the South Side. Louis Outlaw was our lieutenant and he had been in OFI for a few years. He was up for the first run and told the ATF agents to put their gear into 464, and they responded to the fire.

I finished writing my reports just before noon, and Captain Moran asked me to drive him to city hall to deliver some documents to the fire commissioner's office.

I asked Matt what he thought of the federal agents. He said, "These guys have been around, Cos. They have been trained at the University of Maryland on fire behavior, arson, and cause and origin. This is part of a two-year training schedule, and now they have to finish by going to some one hundred fires in Chicago with OFI. They are very professional and we can learn a lot from them. But, they will also learn a lot from us, because we are firefighters. ATF will send about fifty agents through OFI in the next two years."

Matt and I had a beef sandwich on Taylor Street for lunch, and returned to the firehouse on Michigan Avenue.

Engine Company 42 caught a fire at 2037, and pulled a box as soon as they arrived on the scene. Agents Maroca and Malooly had their fire gear in my car, number 463. We responded to Engine 42's fire at 111 West Huron. The radio was blaring and Chief Widell of the First Battalion was telling the Main Fire Alarm Office that heavy smoke was emanating from the windows of the fourth floor of a twelve-story high-rise building.

Upon our arrival at the scene, the firefighters were putting the one hundred foot aerial ladder to the building and leading out lines up into the building and also the outside fire escape. There were people all over the place. This building was the Wacker Hotel, with 320 rental units. By the time we got up to the fire floor, most of the fire was extinguished. Engines 98 and 42 were washing down the three rooms that were involved. I returned to the first floor with the ATF agents.

We started interviewing the occupants of the building. It did not take very long before Maroca found out that the apartment involved was occupied by an employee of the hotel. The night manager informed us that he had had a fire this afternoon, and he had been drinking heavily all day. He also had said he would get even with the owner.

We interviewed the first firefighter who entered the burning rooms. He stated that most of the fire was coming from the bed and mattress in the apartment. When the manager approached the occupant of the subject apartment, and told him there was a fire in his apartment, he jumped up and said, "I didn't do anything!" and ran out of the lobby.

After a thorough fire scene investigation and the elimination of all accidental and natural sources of ignition, the cause of this fire was determined to be of incendiary origin, perpetrated by a former disgruntled employee of the hotel. This employee utilized an open flame and ignited the bedding and other class A combustibles.

Jack Malooly got the suspect's name, age, and approximate height and weight. He noted the color of his hair, his mustache, and his black leather jacket and penny loafer shoes. I remembered what Matt had said, "We will learn how to interview from these guys. They have to log a hundred fires." Well, they got seven from our shift on their first day.

With all the work the union was doing to negotiate a new contract these past few months, a new issue had arisen. Retired firefighters, paramedics, and police officers who risked their lives for the city were very worried about their future. Chicago city government officials had mismanaged the retirees' health-care programs. Everyone knew that healthcare costs across this nation were rapidly rising. However, the city officials who got paid to take care of planning for rising costs dropped the ball. They should have foreseen this situation, and failed to plan appropriately.

So now that a problem had arisen, these highly paid creative officials came up with a very unique solution. They abruptly eliminated the city's contribution to our retirees' healthcare plans. What a great idea!, I thought to myself. Asshole bureaucrats. None of them could do a hard day's work.

Of course, not one of these officials wanted to accept the responsibility for a budget shortfall or a property tax increase. So they figured a way to erase the shortfall. Take it from our retirees and widows by eliminating the city's contribution, and raising the retirees' and widows' premiums by as much as 300 percent! Did they think that this would fly without being seen by our executive board members, who immediately rallied to the cause to turn this crisis around? They asked this question, "Why do firefighters and paramedics need a contract, and a union?" Back in the old days firefighters were not making a decent living and had no healthcare. They had tough times between paying rent and mortgages, paying for food and medical bills to hospitals. We can't and won't return to those days of being the pawns for these city bureaucrats!

Captain Moran came into the kitchen like always, to tell his marshals that the National Fire Protection Association (NFPA) was going to have a class at the Fire Academy. The class was a seminar in fire investigation and field information. It was to help us interview witnesses and victims at fire scenes.

Captain Moran encouraged us to attend this seminar, and also informed us that Chief Alletto insisted we all would participate. The class starts at 0900 and it is my day off, but I needed all the help I could get. As I was signing up for the class, someone said, "Who's up for the run?" I answered, "Four-six-four." Pat Burns said, "You have a still and box alarm at 1439 West Fifty-first Street."

I grabbed my radio and marked down the time of 1150, and the address. As I was responding, I could hear the chief of the Nineteenth Battalion giving orders to the box alarm companies about where to place their rigs at the fire scene.

As I was driving westbound on Fifty-first Street, I could see the heavy black smoke rising up into the clear blue sky. I wondered what was burning. It was a beautiful day, the temperature was about seventy degrees, and the wind was out of the east at thirteen miles per hour. I parked the OFI sedan on Fifty-first about a half block away from the fire.

I reported to Chief Mike Murphy of the Nineteenth Battalion. He said to his driver, Joe Madden, "Look who's here, Inspector Clousseau." Chief Murphy was a friend of mine. We had worked together on the east side for many years.

"What do you know for sure?" I asked. Chief Murphy informed me that, upon his arrival on the scene, fire was issuing from the windows on the first floor in the rear of the building. He also stated that the fire had communicated to the structures on both sides. Engine Company 123 had a two-and-a-half-inch hose line in the gangway on the west side of the burning building, and Truck 39 had Engine 123's second line on the east side. They were making progress, but there was still a lot of fire and smoke issuing from the three-story wooden structure.

In the rear, Engine 116 had two hose lines, playing their streams on the back porches and a convent to the east.

I thought to myself, how did a fire get going like this in the middle of the day? There must be some type of accelerant. Firefighters were working frantically on the roof in an effort to ventilate the heavy smoke. With three structures involved, a 2-11 alarm was called. I talked with one of the sisters from the convent. She stated that the occupant had alerted her of the fire and she called the fire department.

As the 2-11 companies were arriving, hose lines lines were being stretched for Snorkel 5 as they were raising their basket. The Chicago police had Fifty-first Street blocked off in both directions.

Firefighters from Engine 50 and Truck 18 were starting to enter through the front door of the first floor. There were people on the other side of the street and I asked them if anyone had seen the occupant of the first floor. No one seemed to know the identity of that occupant.

After about an hour of exhausting work, the firefighters had most of the fire in the center structure extinguished. The fires in the two buildings on either side were now also extinguished. They did a great job, considering that all three structures were of wood frame construction.

In the rear, Chief Murphy showed me a green garden hose lying by the rear porch. The water was running. Murphy said, "That's a sure sign someone was fighting the fire before they called the fire department."

Standing in the alley behind the buildings was the occupant, Mr. Roderick. As Chief Murphy and I approached him, he said he needed an ambulance. I asked him why. He said he had "smoke inhalation." I told him we would call for the ambulance, but first we needed to know what happened. He was very reluctant to tell us anything at first, and repeated that he had smoke inhalation and needed an ambulance.

This guy no more had smoke inhalation than the man in the fucking moon. I tried a new approach and asked him who was using the garden hose on the fire. He wouldn't answer, and I persisted, "Whoever that was is a hero, because they stopped the fire from extending to the other buildings."

All of a sudden he said, "You mean I am a hero?"

Chief Murphy looked at me and then told Mr. Roderick, "Yeah, you're a hero."

"What was burning when you started putting out the fire?" I asked.

"The fire was coming out of the backdoor," he said, "then I ran to get help and took the garden hose and started trying to put out the fire."

"That was very good sir" I said, "but who lives in the first-floor apartment?"

He said, "I do." I asked him if he knew how the fire started. "Nope, I don't know."

"Were you in your house today?" I asked.

He said, "No, not for a few hours." He said he was spraying for roaches.

I said "Roaches? What were you spraying with?"

He answered quickly, "I didn't do anything. The landlord wouldn't do anything about the roaches. Now, I want an ambulance, because I got smoke inhalation." I told him that he wasn't going to get an ambulance, but what he was going to get was a police officer, and a ride to the police district station.

I went inside the burned-out structure to see if there was any evidence of arson, knowing that, in the meantime, police Officer Hernandez would keep a good eye on Mr. Roderick.

There was heavy charring throughout the first floor, but the most severe fire damage was in a bedroom on the west side of the first floor. Firefighters were pulling at the ceiling and side walls with their pike poles. Hot embers were falling to the floor as I made my way toward the front door.

Firefighters were standing by the front door, but could not go out because the snorkel was washing down the small fire that still remained under the eaves of the structure. The water spray falling along the outside of the structure was just like a waterfall. The noise was almost deafening as the stream of water from the snorkel hit the stairs in front.

This was a scene that I remembered so well, standing out vividly in my mind from years ago, when I was on Truck 15 and Chief Alletto, who was then the captain of Snorkel 3, was directing a solid stream of water in the same way.

As I returned to Mr. Roderick and the policeman, I asked him what could have started on fire in his bedroom on the first floor. Again he said he didn't know. I asked him what type of roach spray he was using to kill the roaches, and again he said he didn't know. With a wink of my eye toward the policeman, I said we had better take this guy into the police station because he won't cooperate. The officer said, "Okay, sir, come with me." All of a sudden, Mr. Roderick wanted to cooperate.

Again I asked him what type of roach spray he used. He said it wasn't a spray it was a roach bomb!

"You mean a sulfur candle," I asked.

He said, "A smoke bomb, sir." He informed me that you place this little can on the floor and light it with a match.

The fire was out now, and I reentered the first-floor apartment. The firefighters were picking up their hoses, and I asked Captain Gene Bedore if a couple of guys could help me look for these little cans of sulfur bombs.

We started digging through the fire debris on the floor in the bedroom and sure as hell one of the fireman said, "Hey, is this what you're looking for?" as he handed me a small can.

Yes, I told him, that's what I'm looking for. Then two more cans were brought out from the bedroom. The section of the greatest damage was along the south wall of this bedroom where the remains of a dresser was located.

I showed the cans to Chief Murphy and the rest of the firemen standing in the apartment. The fire was struck out and Engines 116, 123, and 50 were rolling their hoses, and preparing for the next hit.

I told the police officer about the cans, and asked Mr. Roderick how many cans he had lit. He said six cans, three in the bedroom and two in the kitchen. I just looked at him for a minute. I wanted to say something, but I just turned and walked away.

Three buildings destroyed by fire because of a person who did not use a little common sense. After the elimination of all other causes, I determined that this fire was, in fact, accidental with the cause being the result of improper placement of exterminating sulfur candles by the occupant, Mr. Roderick.

It was after four in the afternoon before I returned to 1401 South Michigan. The day shift was gone except for Lieutenant Mike Deckelmann.

"Cos, what did you have over there on Fifty-first Street," Mike asked.

"Sulfur candles under the bedroom dresser," I answered.

Mike asked me if I thought it was a deliberately set fire, because you know they do that.

"No," I said, "this guy was too dumb to think up something like that!"

No, he had nothing to gain. He was renting the apartment. After writing the report, I couldn't stop thinking about what Deckelmann said. What a way to set a fire.

Most of the marshals went to the Fire Academy the next day for the class that was put on by NFPA. It was very interesting the way the speaker told us how to interview witnesses, owners, and occupants like Mr. Roderick. A two-day seminar and another certificate, and then back to the firehouse.

For once, you could almost say that everyone in the firehouse was happy, or they appeared to be happy. Local 2 and the city of Chicago had finished negotiations and the firefighters had a new four-year contract! They are calling it a new beginning with the city. Acting Mayor Eugene Sawyer, Fire Commissioner Louis Galante, Union President Martin O. Holland, and the Local 2 Executive Board announced the four-year contract at a press conference.

This contract offered firefighters and paramedics excellent pay raises. With this new mayor, we were able to ratify a multi-year contract. With all of the problems within the city hall and with an election for mayor next year, we won't have to negotiate again for three years.

A lump sum of $1,250 cash and a 16.5 percent raise in four years. That sure will help out at the "home office," my house. Local 2 also won more in fringe benefits, like furlough selections and trades, holiday pay on a Daley day and much more. I know there was a lot of work and long hours put into getting this contract approved both by the city and our membership.

In the old days, a handshake was what we got, and at the time it was okay. Mayor Richard J. Daley's word was his bond. Today, however, we live in a different day and time. Everything has to be written down in black and white in a contract. Some people say why do you need a union? Ask yourself this question: If your employers did not have anyone to question or oppose them, do you really think they would just give you dental or vision insurance? We won a good package! The firefighters' union learned a bitter lesson during the strike, however. Don't take anyone's word!

Matt sat us down in the kitchen, and after talking about the contract, he said there were a few things in OFI we needed to talk about. Collecting physical evidence at a fire scene was number one. If the cause of the fire is accidental, don't take any evidence. This basement is full of shit, or should I say evidence, that will never be used in a court of law.

"Marshals," he said, "whenever you determine a fire to be incendiary, let the police officers that are on the scene, secure the evidence." That way if the Bomb and Arson cannot respond in a timely manner, the police are stuck waiting for the B and A and not you. "They are a bunch of fucking prima donnas who think the fire marshals are stupid. But you know what? The fact of the matter is that we have the necessary technical expertise to document the events that came together to cause a fire and they lack this technical knowledge. They try to mask their shortcomings with public relations bullshit!"

Matt continued, "Oh yeah, another thing: when you get gas at Eleventh and State, they will need a photo ID card. That's all men. Be careful out there, it's a jungle." We all were laughing as Matt walked out of the kitchen. He was funny, but sharp.

All I thought about was the new contract, and the money, of course. A raise every year without asking for one. I liked that.

I thought to myself, this investigation work is getting very interesting, although I still miss breaking windows and getting a fresh breath of air during a smoky fire. OFI is working out for me. I am still going to fires, and a lot of them. When an engine company pulls up and says "we got smoke" and I am up for the run because of the rotation, a knot seems to form in my gut. Then the adrenaline begins to flow. When the engine company yells, "Emergency-give us a box!" and you're running on full adrenaline as you respond, it's a great feeling. Fire cause investigation is a real challenge. It makes you think critically, as Chief Alletto would say.

Chapter 4

THE SUMMER OF 1988 CAME IN JUST LIKE MANY OTHER SUMMERS, WITH hot days and nights, and the fires continued. One morning in July, Peggy called and asked if I could come to her side of the office by the rear door. There was a new guy from ATF who was going to begin riding with OFI. He has to get one hundred fires documented just like John Maroca and Jack Malooly. Peggy introduced us and informed me that he was from Minnesota, and they called him Rogie, "no name," only Rogie.

Just like any other firehouse, we had housework. We cleaned and vacuumed the locker room, and washrooms were cleaned every day. I tried to show this ATF agent a little about the housework, but after he made his bunk he went back downstairs. To my surprise, Rogie made a fresh pot of coffee and cleaned the cups from earlier this morning. That was nice of him.

Jack was up for the first run, so Rogie put on his fire gear in Jack's sedan, 463, and told us one thing he would like to do was eat at the Taste of Chicago. We told him sure, but later.

The temperature was going to be going up to one hundred degrees, with the humidity at 85 percent. Jack left to fill up his car with gas and Rogie went with him.

Lewis Outlaw was the lieutenant today. He was in 464, and I was in 465. The first still and box came in about 1030, and I heard Jack repeat the address to the Main Fire Alarm Office and tell them that he was taking in the still and box somewhere in Logan Square, on the northwest side of the city.

Lewis is now up for the run in 464. I went for lunch with Mike Deckelmann to Connie's Pizza. While we were eating, another still and box came in on the West Side. I heard Lewis repeat the address, and tell the Fire Alarm Office that he was taking it in.

I told Deckelmann, "Let's finish, because I am up for the next run. Mike said, "Take it easy, Cos." I said, "If I get a run you're going with me." Mike works on the day shift with Matt, Tom Purdy, Pat Burns, and Chief Alletto. Mike said, "So I will go to another fire, so what?"

We returned to the firehouse on Michigan Avenue. There was only one room that had air conditioning and that was the kitchen. Soon after our return, Jack and Rogie returned in 463. We sat in the cool kitchen and talked about the fire they had just returned from, in Logan Square. I must have dozed off a little in my chair, because the next thing I heard was that familiar ring of the red phone.

I grabbed the phone and answered "Cosgrove, OFI." "Cosgrove, this is the Main Fire Alarm Office. We need an OFI car to respond to a still and box at 1454 West School Street."

I repeated the address and told him that 465 would respond. I looked up at the clock-1432. "Hey, Rogie, we gotta run," I yelled, while I took my portable radio from the charger.

I jumped into the car and told Rogie to get the overhead door. I checked my street guide for School Street. It is 3300 North and I know Loomis is 1400 West. "Take the Outer Drive," someone yelled. "We'll close the overhead door."

Lake Shore Drive was mostly open this time of day, and I was making good time responding with lights and siren. I listened to the radio:

"Battalion Five is on the scene, and we have a fire in a three-story wood-frame building."

"Who's my engines?" the chief yelled.

"Engine 55 to Battalion Five, we're pulling up on School."

He yelled again, "Get a deck gun on it now." Then I heard, "Battalion Five to Main, emergency! Give me a 2-11, Office."

The Fire Alarm Office replied, "Battalion Five, you got a 2-11!"

As I turned of off Lake Shore Drive at Belmont, you could see the smoke in the distant sky. Fire equipment was arriving from all directions. I parked the car on Jansen Street east of the fire, and we donned our fire coats, boots, and helmets and walked west toward the burning structure.

Firefighters were raising ladders to the front of the concerned structure. Firefighters from Engine 78 were manning a two-and-a-half-inch hose line protecting the exposures to the east. As I walked around the west side of the burning structure on Greenview Avenue, fire was issuing from the rear roof area toward the alley. The temperature is a clean ninety-seven degrees and there is no wind. The heavy smoke fell right back into the faces of the firefighters who were raising the main ladder of Truck 13 on Greenview.

Truck 44 was opening the steep gable roof in the front of 1458 West School. This fire was far from over, and the ATF agent's eyes were wide open. I finally caught up to Chief Dwyer of the Fifth Battalion and asked him about occupants. He said he had no idea.

Conditions at this fire grew worse because of the extremely hot weather. A relief lieutenant from the Second District fell to the street from heat exhaustion. The lieutenant was transported to Illinois Masonic Hospital by Ambulance 48.

Firefighters were up on the second floor with their lines. You could hear glass breaking all around the structure as they ventilated the second and third floors of the burning structure, to release the hot gases and heavy smoke.

The smoke then started to clear. It had been reported to a police officer that someone was barbecuing on the rear deck of the corner building. I entered the building and went up to the second floor. Firefighters were pulling ceilings and side walls throughout the second and third floors. You can't be sure in a wood-framed building. If in doubt, pull it down. I made my way out what was a sliding glass door that led out to a roof deck in the rear of this second-floor apartment.

Sure enough, there was a Weber type barbecue grill over to the side, but it hadn't been used today. There was still unburned charcoal inside the grill.

As I looked over this roof type deck that had been destroyed by this fire, I couldn't find an ignition source in this area that appeared to be where this fire originated. People said that the whole rear deck area was on fire. The interior of the front of the second-floor apartment appeared to have less severe damage. No damage was found around the living room to the south.

As I made my way back toward the kitchen that led out to this deck, the damage got worse. I went down to the first floor. Water was running down the walls and dripping from the flooring above, but the fire damage was less than the second floor.

I met two detectives from Bomb and Arson. They had responded to this 2-11 alarm. One of them said, "Hi, my name is Tim O'Meara. I'm a detective in B and A. What have you found out so far?"

"Bill Cosgrove from OFI, and this is a Special Agent from ATF, and I haven't found out shit as yet."

O'Meara told me that someone had heard someone jump off the roof deck and then there was heavy smoke coming from up there (pointing to the roof deck).

I informed O'Meara that I had looked over the second floor and did not see anything that could ignite a fire up there. He told me he wanted to take a look.

I decided to go for some water or anything cold. Over on School Street, the Salvation Army Disaster Service is set up and I called out to Rogie, my ATF agent, who was just in awe by everything that had just happened. He was from a small town in Minnesota and had never witnessed a fire like this one. Lemonade was the cold drink for the day, and it was good. I talked to some of the firemen by the Salvation Army wagon, who were now enjoying their cold drinks. The guys from Engine 78 said they tried to cover the exposure to the east, but the fire got in a little in the rear. I took my lemonade and walked around the alley behind the fire building.

There was another wooden-framed building about an arm's length away from what I thought was the original fire building. Outside in the yard area firefighters had thrown out a chair that had been severely burned. I entered the rear door that had been forced open by firefighters from Squad 2 and Engine 106.

The kitchen area was covered by smoke and there was a line of demarcation around the top portion of the room. There was a small bedroom off the kitchen that had been severely burned by the fire. I could see where the chair had been that was now in the yard and alongside was a vacuum cleaner and the remains of a wooden table. Across the small bedroom was a dresser in front of a window. The bed was not burned at all.

I went between the buildings to about the area where the

window was located. There was a perfect pattern in the siding leading up to where the roof deck was located. I returned to the interior bedroom again and moved the small dresser out from the wall. There on the floor were the remnants of drapes or curtains still smoldering and glass that had fallen inward.

The burn patterns clearly indicated that this fire originated in this bedroom, most likely in the stuffed chair in the backyard.

I returned to the Salvation Army wagon where I met with ATF Agent Rogie. He was talking to my boss, Chief Pat Burns, who responded on the 2-11 alarm.

"Marshal," Chief Burns said, "they say this might be a set fire. Someone heard someone jump off this deck." Then I told Pat what I had found in the other building. We all went to take a look and Pat agreed with me that this fire originated in the stuffed chair. The two B and A detectives were notified that this fire originated inside the bedroom of 1454 West School Street, and not on the roof deck as thought earlier. Both of the B and A detectives, after seeing the evidence, agreed with my findings. Detective Timothy O'Meara paid me a nice compliment for finding the origin of this fire. I thanked him.

After interviews were conducted, it was discovered that the person who called the fire department first saw fire between the two structures. The occupant of the one-bedroom apartment told us she had been smoking a cigarette just before she left for work at about 1200.

Most of the fire companies were returning to their quarters and Engines 55 and 106 were bedding their hose, and we were returning to 1401 South Michigan. Rogie was going on about how the firefighters were worked so hard in this extreme heat, in order to extinguish this fire. Again he asked if we could eat at the Taste of Chicago. I said, "Sure, but first we have to do some paperwork."

After writing the report that this fire was the result of a "misuse of smoking materials," I took a much needed shower and at about 1930 we went to the Taste of Chicago.

The Taste of Chicago is a great attraction in the summer. It runs for about one week and millions of people visit the lakefront for the many different types of food, and entertainment. I was not very hungry, but I knew that if I got to the Taste, I would get corn on the cob. Rogie wanted to try everything! I parked the red and black sedan on the corner of Balbo and Columbus on the sidewalk. I explained to Rogie that we are in service and if we get separated, meet me at the car. As we entered the south end of the Taste, it did not take long before we were mingling with a huge crowd of people. Again I told Rogie to stay close, because if we missed a run, we would have to explain this to Chief Alletto. We walked along the curb on the east side of Columbus. We figured a way to work this. If I saw something I wanted to try, or Rogie did, then we went toward the vendor, got our food and returned to the curb to eat the food.

It did not take too long before I found the corn on the cob vendor. Rogie said he wanted something else, so I went to the vendor, got my corn, and returned to the curb. People were everywhere and now Rogie said he was going in for a steak sandwich.

I waited on the curb as planned, eating my corn on the cob. I was keeping a good eye on this guy from ATF. I wondered to myself what he must be thinking about all this, a big fire this afternoon, and now thousands of people at the Taste of Chicago. I finished my corn, and threw the cob in the trash basket. As I looked over to the steak vendor's booth, I did not see Rogie. I looked along the curb where we planned to meet-no Rogie. Oh, man. He had on a white T-shirt, but so did about a thousand other people. The search for my missing agent went on for over an hour. I returned to the car, but no Rogie. What the hell am I going to do if I get a run? Well, as I was walking along the curb, Rogie steps out of a row of bushes and says, "Hey, Cos, where did you go?"

"Where did I go?" I exclaimed. "You idiot, I was on the fucking curb."

He could see I was upset, and told me he saw an antique fire truck over there pointing to the other side of the row of bushes. It doesn't matter, because we are out of here. If I blow a run, I'll be in shit up to my ass.

After returning to the firehouse, I felt bad about getting upset at Rogie. He was from a small town in northern Minnesota, and probably had never seen as many people as he saw at the Taste of Chicago.

Rogie asked me about the Salvation Army's Canteen that had served the cold lemonade at the fire. Do they go to all fires? No, I told him, just to 2-11 alarms or better, and special incidents where firefighters will be working for a long time. They provide firefighters with coffee and soup when it's cold out, and refreshing lemonade and sandwiches when it's hot out. They began this tradition in 1953 and have been responding to incidents ever since. I remember a time when I was cold and wet at a fire scene. There was this truck that they called a "canteen" about a half block from the fire. They gave us dry warm gloves, hot coffee and, if you wanted, a cigarette. So whenever I see one of those people standing in front of a store around Christmas, if they are part of the Salvation Army, I always put some money in their pot and remember the warm gloves, hot soup and coffee. They are great people.

Chapter 5

Finally, after almost ten months, it was my turn to attend the classes for the state of Illinois' Fire Investigation Modules. I would be going with a firefighter that I worked with on Truck Company 15, Joe Kinnerk. The class would be held up north at the Fort Sheridan Army Installation.

After you finished with the modules, you then were "certified" by the state of Illinois. There were about fifty people in our class who were firefighters and police officers. We learned ways to determine whether a fire was accidental or incendiary. What motivates a fire setter and also insurance laws, and the arson statutes. I met police officers from Bomb and Arson in Chicago. Compared to many of the others in our class, we were dealing with arson and all kinds of other fires every day. This class lasted two weeks. At first I thought it was hard because we had tests all the time, but we learned things the right way, and I did well.

They taught us different ways to write our fire reports and take field notes. It's not that Matt Moran and Chief Alletto didn't teach us right, but in the modules they have different teachers for each subject, and we got a feel for their way.

There are ways to investigate fires where the occupants could not get out, and then lost their lives. Fatal fires take a lot more investigation work than a fire without injury or death. You must have documentation and justify your conclusions, since there is a good possibility that you will be subpoenaed to testify in a criminal or civil proceeding.

Fort Sheridan was an ideal place to take the modules, because there were many abandoned buildings on the base. We had live burns where they set a fire and then we came back into the building to investigate the fire. It helped you to correctly read various types of burn patterns and follow them back to the point of origin.

Although Fort Sheridan was a very long ride for Joe Kinnerk and me, we got a lot from the class. Some of my favorites were photography and sketching where you learned not to get too close or too far away with the camera. Just little tricks to make you do your job better.

Probably the most important part of the modules was the law part. A lot of time was dedicated to the criminal code from chapter 38. The reason we spent so much time on how the law works with fire investigation is that it all comes down to the courtroom, and if you are not conversant with the law, you might look like a dummy when testifying in court.

If you conduct a fire investigation and you miss something, like eliminating all other sources of ignition before arriving at a determination, or not taking photos, or not taking the proper procedures when collecting and securing evidence, when the case goes to court the opposing counsel will do everything to impeach your credibility. Your testimony may be thrown out and you might lose your case.

After two weeks of classroom and field study, we were given an examination of what we had learned. I was very surprised by my score. I received an 88 for my final mark. This really pleased me, and I felt that I had lived up to Chief Alletto's expectations.

I returned to OFI and the firehouse. It was nice in a way to be away from all the fires and reports, but now I was very eager to start back to work. I could now put some of the new things to the test that I had learned at the modules. We had only finished the first part of the modules, and in the month of October we would return to take the third module, and if we successfully completed all three modules, the state of Illinois would issue a certified Fire Investigator credential.

I got in early on my next workday, and the third platoon were all very busy writing fire reports. The lieutenant, Walter Burke, had to be the first to give me a shot.

"We can all go home now, men, because Cos finished his modules, and can take all the fires," he said. A big laugh came from the other two marshals, Jim Voris and Don Rimgale.

One of the first things I asked was if there had been many fires. They all looked at each other and Rimgale says, "we had thirteen runs yesterday, Cos." Jim Voris said, "Cos I had a fire with four points of origin, and the fires were set by a cat."

Jim Voris was a good investigator, and had some complex cases with death or maybe a large fire, loss.

Matt walked into the kitchen and said, "Marshals, we had 158 fires last month. Of all of them, there were 87 that were determined incendiary." It was good to be back. Chief Alletto congratulated me on my test scores from the modules and welcomed me back. He was a tough but really fair boss, and very well respected by the marshals and the firefighters in the field.

Matt informed us the Dan Ryan Expressway would close all of the local lanes for the next two months, so when we were responding to fires, we had to be sure not to get caught in traffic.

We were to use the main streets until this resurfacing project was completed. He added, "If it's late or very early in the morning, I think you will make some time responding, but be careful, Marshals, on the Dan Ryan."

We had four guys working on my first day back from the modules, and so I had a partner, Bob Villanueva. He was also a firefighter, and had about eleven years on the job.

Bob told me he had to finish a report from the day before, so I checked out 464, the car we would be working in, and put my fire gear in the back seat. One of the first things we would have to do is get fuel for the car. After all the runs the third shift had yesterday, there was only about one-eighth of a tank.

It was a nice sunny day in Chicago for the month of October. Most of the leaves had changed colors and started to fall, and as nice as it looked, it was a sure sign that winter was not very far off. After getting fuel, we drove down Michigan Avenue towards the Loop. Just looking at Chicago's magnificent skyscrapers and the beautiful lakefront made me stop and think about what a great city we live in. Bobby and I talked about the great contract that we now had with the city of Chicago.

A firefighter will now make about $36,000 dollars a year, with raises each year of the contract. Drivers of trucks, squads, and tillermen of Hook and Ladders will receive 3 percent for driver's pay. The most astonishing part of this new contract is that we get paid for overtime. You can work your Daley day and it is off a seniority overtime list.

Bob Villanueva told me that being in OFI, he was now losing money, because he had been assigned formerly as the driver of Truck Company 7.

We had the first run of the day in the early afternoon. The fire was in an alley garage in the Twentieth Battalion, and it was accidental in cause. I was a little disappointed because with all my new training from the modules, I was looking for a challenge. Not to worry-there would be more fires.

In the early morning hours on October 4, a still alarm was given to Engines 19 and 16, Truck 11 and the Second Battalion to a fire at 702 East Thirty-eighth Street. Upon their arrival on the scene, smoke and fire was issuing from windows on the second and third floor of a three-story building.

There were people in several windows screaming for help. The lieutenant of Engine 19 called the Main Fire Alarm Office and requested a box alarm. There were victims laying on the sidewalk at the base of the building in the front and the back. While leading out their fire hoses, Engine 19 called for three ambulances for the injured victims. When I arrived on the scene the Second Battalion called the Main Fire Alarm Office and requested a 2-11 alarm and two more ambulances.

There were people calling for help, ladders were being raised and the fire was burning out of control. Firefighters and paramedics were carrying victims to nearby ambulances. Soon the fire was starting to produce white and gray smoke and I knew that they were now hitting fire well and cooling it.

Bob and I split up. I went to the back of the building and Bob started getting names and numbers of how many victims were injured. It looked like most of the fire was in the rear section of the structure on the west end. I talked to a black man who lived on the first floor of the concerned structure. I asked him who lived in the apartment on the second floor. He related that he did not know the man's name, but that he lived alone.

I made my way up the rear stairway to the second floor. Firefighters were pulling down lath and plaster from the ceilings and side walls. Then someone yelled, "Hey, Captain, we got one in here," as the firefighters moved toward the bedroom. One of the guys turned toward me and said, "There's a burn

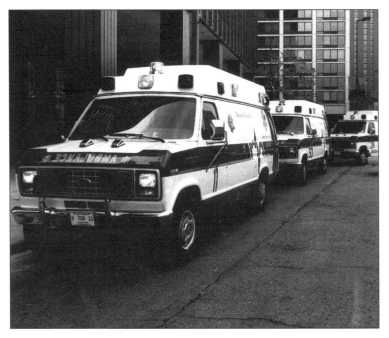

Ambulances in line at Mercy Hospital after a fire.

victim." I called downstairs to the ground floor and requested the photo unit, because I knew he or she would have to be photographed before we moved the body. Chief Buckley walked through the hall leading to the bedroom. He looked at me and said, "Where's the victim?" I pointed to the room where all the firemen were. "Let's get a body bag," the chief yelled. I informed him that we needed to photograph the victim where he was found.

I made my way into the bedroom where the victim was lying alongside the bed and the wall. I took my notebook from under my fire coat and made a fast sketch of the room. The water was falling on the back of my helmet and steam was rising from the bed and the victim. The firefighters were looking at me like I was nuts, as they started to remove the hot debris from the top of the victim. After he was photographed, they carefully put the victim in the body bag, and moved him to an awaiting police wagon in the alley behind the building.

I met up with Bob Villanueva. He told me that six people were taken by ambulance to nearby hospitals. Bob and I returned to the second-floor bedroom, which was the area of origin, to dig through the debris. After removing most of the items in the room we found an electric hot plate next to the bed. After examining this hot plate, we determined that it was plugged into a duplex receptacle and was the cause of this fire.

We returned to the front of the structure and most of the fire companies had returned to their quarters. The injured victims were taken to Mercy Hospital and also to Michael Reese Hospital. We now had to go to these hospitals and get the names, ages, and injuries of the victims from this terrible fire from the medical personnel in the emergency rooms.

At Mercy Hospital, I met with Emergency Medical Service (EMS) Field Officer Mike McKittrick. He informed me we had two victims who had smoke inhalation and four victims with cuts, lacerations, and broken bones. The corpse was taken to the Cook County Morgue and that was our next stop. The firefighters did one hell of a job taking people down ladders and rescuing them from within the burning structure.

Paramedics removed victims on stretchers to their ambulances. After triage evaluations, they transported the victims to the hospitals. As bad as this fire was, firefighters and paramedics working together saved the lives of many people. What a different time we now work in, and so much better because of much better equipment, such as self-contained breathing apparatus.

In our earlier years, there were never enough ambulances when they were needed. And now we not only have the ambulances, we have trained medical personnel (paramedics) that can handle almost any emergency. Not that many years ago, when firefighters were assigned to ambulances throughout Chicago, they did a pretty good job administering first aid or administering oxygen, and a fast ride to the nearest hospital. But that was about all the training they received. Today we have a highly professional EMS division.

I, for one, was very happy to see the beginning of the paramedic program in Chicago. It put an end to placing firefighters in ambulances, who were not trained like new emergency medical technicians and paramedics. But like any organization, they had to prove themselves to many people before they were accepted. I liked sitting around with my brother Mike, Jim Donahue, and Mike McKittrick and listening to the story of how the paramedics made their way into the Chicago Fire Department.

If I remember how these paramedics told the story to me, I think it went something like this. In 1975, the city of Chicago began the process of recruiting emergency medical technicians (EMTs) and paramedics. They were part of the model cities program. After hiring about sixty EMTs they were bounced from one ambulance to the next all around the city. There were no provisions for them at the time, and they did not have any benefits at all. If an EMT was injured on or off the job and could not work, they were just taken off the city's payroll. They had no pension, no rank, and no assignments. In these troubled times, a number of paramedics started their own organization and started fighting the city of Chicago for benefits.

It wasn't until 1976 that they were finally accepted into the city's municipal employees pension fund. In 1977, a new order came out by the fire commissioner, that stated anyone who would want to become an EMT could sign up at the Fire Academy. My brother, Mike, signed up and entered the Chicago Fire Department. He later was assigned to Ambulance 14 in Engine 54's quarters. The paramedics continued their fight and the paramedic-in-charge rank was recognized in 1979. Some paramedics were appointed to the rank of field supervisor.

Also, in 1979, the paramedics were accepted into the Chicago Firefighters' Union, Local 2. The number of ambulances in the city grew and so did the number of paramedics. In 1982, a rank system was established and after a long fight the paramedics were allowed into the firefighters' pension fund, after a bill was passed by the state legislature in 1985. Many firefighters were against this, and Marty Holland took a lot of heat for it.

There are some fifty-three ambulances in the city, and anything that these paramedics have, they had to fight for. In those early days, paramedics had to take a lot of flack in the field. When a chief requested an ambulance to the scene of a fire or a motor vehicle accident, he would say "What the hell took you so long?" Also, when the paramedic called the base station at a hospital to tell them what they had, the chief yelled, "What the hell are you waiting for, this guy could die before you get him to the hospital!" They have come a long way in a few years.

The paramedics gave us the information on all the victims that were transported to Mercy Hospital from the fire on East Thirty-eighth Street. We got back to OFI at 0830 that morning. Bob took care of the injury and fatality cards for the victims of the fire and I took care of the journals. The report, however, would have to wait until the next workday.

Chapter 6

FIREFIGHTERS DON'T JUST GIVE THEIR TIME TO FIGHTING FIRES AND saving lives. After they leave their firehouses they are actually involved in some community projects and reaching out to the citizens of Chicago. For example, here are a few of the projects where they are participating and volunteering their time: Softball tournaments, to aid in raising money for the Cook County Burn Centers Burn Fund; a fundraiser for a needy family with a sick child; a great chili cook—off at Navy Pier that raised over $6,000 for needy children; the Special Olympics, where our brothers and sisters volunteered much of their time; and don't forget the Christmas carolers who sang in front of Marshall Fields downtown to help collect funds for the Salvation Army.

Director Will (the Squire) Danaher is building a strong public relations department for the Chicago Firefighters' Union, Local 2. He finds a good cause and then works hard to get firefighters involved in these community events.

With the cold winter setting in again in Chicago, the month of November had fires at an all time high. "Firefighters are like the Marines," Chief Alletto would say. "No one gives a shit about you, until they need you. Then we're the greatest people in the world. But that's okay, I still love it."

On this particular day, I am working with Jack Lumsden, and so far we have had a pretty slow day. We are up for the next run. After eating a late dinner at a very good restaurant at Forty-sixth and Western, which is one of Jack's favorites, we started back to 1401 South Michigan. We had about a half tank of gas and decided to fill up at the Area 1 Police Headquarters at Fifty-first and Wentworth Avenue before we returned to the firehouse.

At 2130, Engines 19 and 29, and Hook and Ladders 11 and 4, and the Second Battalion responded to a fire at 3547 South Federal. Upon their arrival on the scene, fire and smoke was issuing from the windows on the fifteenth floor.

"Engine 19 to Main," the officer called over the radio, "Emergency-give us a box."

Jack turned on the lights and told the Main Fire Alarm Office that 463 was responding to the box alarm. The firefighters immediately faced their first problem. The elevators in the building were out of service. With two-and-a-half-inch hose lines, one-and-three-quarter-inch hose lines, hand pumps, pike poles, and axes in hand, they began the long climb up to the fifteenth floor! The second problem they faced was that the standpipe system also was out of service and had been since 1985. The Chicago Housing Authority has had a poor record of maintaining standpipe systems in all their buildings, and this has had a very negative impact on firefighting in those buildings.

As the firefighters were ascending to the fifteenth floor, a citizen, Mr. Jackson, from within the building, forced entry into the burning apartment. Just inside the door, Mr. Jackson found two young children between the ages of two and three years old, and took them to safety. The fire had gained headway, and had spread into the hall as the firefighters completed their overwhelming climb.

With a shortness of breath, Firefighter Mick Halloran of

Engine 29 entered the burning apartment. On his hands and knees and with a pike pole, he broke the first window inside the door. Right on his ass is Firefighter Jimmy "Krow" Krouladis, and he dropped 150 feet of hose down the outside of the building to the ground. The firefighters on the ground had made a conventional lead out to the base of the building with a three-inch line. The hook-up was quickly made, and they sent the water.

We arrived on the scene within a few minutes of the still alarm companies. I told Jack I would go up and he didn't argue. I started getting on my gear. As I looked up at the building, I could see flames and black smoke billowing from the windows on the fifteenth floor. After finding out that there were no elevators, I started my long climb. This really irritated me. It was very hard on the firefighters, and made their job so much more difficult!

It brought back a lot of memories from when I worked on Cottage Grove. I climbed steadily at first, until I arrived on the seventh floor and then the climb got slower. I met up with Chief Baldwin of the Second Battalion. He said, "I am getting too old for this shit." I said, "Yeah, me too," as I huffed and puffed past him.

By the time I reached the fire floor, the firefighters of the Second Battalion were in the burning apartment. Most of the fire had been extinguished and hot steam and smoke emanated out the door of a bedroom. Through the smoke in the room I saw Firefighter Michael Halloran carrying something in his arms. "Cos," he said, "it's a baby!"

I shined my light on him and what looked like a one-year-old infant. His face told the whole story, blackened by smoke, with a certain sadness in his eyes that a fireman only has when a child dies in a fire.

In the bedroom Jimmy Krow is still washing down the burned contents of the room. He said, "Cos, these fucking CHA buildings, there isn't one good thing about them. We tried hard to get into this apartment and it was hot."

"I know, Jim, it was one hell of a lead out," I said.

"We do this all the time in the projects," he said, "because the standpipe systems are out of service in all these buildings."

The infant was taken down to a police wagon. I went to apartment 1504 where the other children had been taken. We found out that they were left alone while the mother went to get a pack of cigarettes. In an interview, the kids told us they had been playing with matches in the bedroom.

Chief Baldwin had called the Chicago police and the mother was arrested and taken to the Area 1 police station. The fire was determined accidental with the cause being unattended children playing with matches. We returned to quarters and wrote up the violations. No elevators, no standpipe system, and no smoke detectors in apartment 1501. I would have liked to give an award to the firefighters of Engine 29 for their unique way of leading out fire hose in the projects. They surely deserve an "attaboy" for a job well done.

Why do kids light fires? Well, here's what I have found out in this short time in OFI. Very young children are attracted to fire and fire setting very much. Curiosity is the main reason that children play with matches or lighters. Fire fascinates kids, and it may even frighten them, but curiosity is the driving force that makes them light matches.

While it is not unusual for kids to find fire interesting, they don't know that fire causes indescribable destruction and sometimes death, like the fire we just came from in the projects. In most cases, this curious fire setter is a boy, and he wants to see the fire, and how it looks, and how it burns. Most of the fires that involve children occur during the daytime hours, and the reason is that this child is unattended or unsupervised. A one-year-old infant died tonight in a fire. Not because his three-year-old brother was playing with matches, but because his mother left them alone while she went down to the corner for cigarettes. It's a tremendous tragedy.

The second shift begins to filter into the firehouse at 0700. It was Thanksgiving Day, and I was off for this holiday, looking forward to a big turkey dinner with my wife and kids. It's not too bad being in the firehouse on Thanksgiving, because there is a club and you are with your other family. But in OFI there is no club, and no turkey. You just find some restaurant and hopefully you're able to eat before you get a run. I was glad that I was off duty today, after a night like we just had.

The holiday season was here again, and so was the cold weather. It is a time of happiness and good cheer but it is simply amazing what happens to people during the holiday season. For some who love to shop it's great, but to some, the holiday season is a very depressing time. People act crazy and the suicide rate increases. No one knows this better than a firefighter, paramedic, or a police officer.

People must like to crash into each other because they do it every day with the first snowfall of the year. Just a few inches causes havoc on the roads. After a day or two, people slow down and respect the slippery pavement. Then we all move from place to place a little slower, and are more careful. But it takes much longer to get to where you are going. People begin to lose their tempers and more 9-1-1 calls are made.

We were back in the firehouse, the first platoon was coming in and the third platoon was going home. Tony Maritato was my partner, and we were in 464. The rig is another shop reject with about 120,000 miles on the odometer. Rimgale told Tony it has a good heater, but the oil light stays on, and other than that, it's a fucking piece of junk. "So, men, have a nice day," he says as he removes his wet fire coat from the back seat.

Louis Outlaw was filling out the journal for the day. Matt walked into the kitchen headed for the coffee pot and his morning talk.

"Marshals," he said, "there are three undetermined fires on my desk. We all know what happens with undetermined fires, don't we?" In a loud voice he continued, "That means I have to now conduct a follow-up investigation! I have to go out to the fire scene all by myself and try to find out what happened and how the fuck it happened. Then I have to return back here and write a report about your fire. Remember, Marshals, when I came on this job you always took good care of your captain, and you guys are not taking care of your captain!" He was shouting now. We all just laughed because Matt was a funny guy.

"There are a lot more fires," Matt continued, on a serious note. "People are getting cold and they start turning up the thermostats on space heaters, stoves, and those very old heating systems in their homes. It seems like arson is still among the top causes for fires lately in Chicago."

Matt said, "Take your hate fire setter-he set the fire because he was jealous and angry at his friend. So he burned the whole fucking building down. This is what we call twisted thinking, and he must be stamped out, men."

"I would guess that one of Matt's follow-ups is a hate fire and that's why we just heard all that shit," Tony said, and Matt gave me the eye, turned, and left the kitchen.

I have known Matt for years, and took the wink as "let's talk." He said, "Marshal, meet me at this follow-up. I need a hand with digging through the fire debris."

"Sure, Marshal," I said. "When do you want me to go with you?"

"The fire scene is on the West Side," Matt said, "in Engine 44's still district and I won't get there until ten or ten thirty. I will call you on the radio." I gave him a big 10-4 and he laughed.

Tony and I left to get gas at the police headquarters at Eleventh and State. If we don't fill up now, we may have to later with no gas around, which has happened before.

Matt called us on the radio, and said he was just leaving the Eleventh Police District on West Harrison Street. He gave us the address of the fire and told us to meet him. It was a gloomy afternoon on West Flournoy Street, with people still removing anything they can salvage from yesterday's fire.

No wonder Matt wanted a little company, this is a bad-ass street, and one guy to investigate a fire that was a 2-11 alarm is dangerous. Matt informed us that the police have a guy they like for arson on this fire. He said that the fire started in the basement, and the B and A detectives say that it originated on the stairs outside the basement. As we made our way around the burned-out structure, we find the rear wooden porches were almost consumed by the fire, and structural members that were left were also heavily charred.

After putting on our fire gear, we entered through the front door, and continued up to the first-floor apartment. Most of the fire damage was in the rear toward the kitchen. Burn patterns on the window casings and door jamb indicated that this fire traveled from the outside rear porches into the kitchens on all three floors.

"We have to check the basement," Matt said.

I stepped off the bottom stair into about a foot of water from the fire yesterday, and with our flashlights probing ahead of us we made our way to the back of the basement. You could see that the fire had burned the floor joists on the southwest section. There was heavy charring on the floor joist.

"Check that door," Matt said, "and see if it was open at the time of the fire." Tony made his way through the water toward the door.

Tony said, "Yeah, the door was open, there is charring on the inside of the door jamb," indicating it was not protected, as it would have been if the door was closed. Matt made his way toward Tony and asked where the charring was. Tony directed his light beam on the door jamb.

"That's it for us. Let's get some photos and get the hell out of here, Marshals," Matt said. "The fire originated in the basement, and that is all we are concerned with. Thank you for backing me up. I will see you back at quarters," and we all left the scene.

Tony said, "How about something to eat? I sure can go for a hot dog from Donald's on Western Ave."

While we were eating our hot dogs, Engine 65 got an automatic call from ADT for a water flow alarm. "Engine 65 to Englewood," crackled on the fire radio. I can hear the voice of Mike Hill. He is the lieutenant on Engine 65 today. "We are on the scene, 3729 South Saint Louis. We have a little smoke showing in a two-story brick factory, 300 by 500 feet, and water flowing out of a service door.

Tony said, "That's just a water flow, they won't need OFI," and we started to return to our firehouse. A few minutes later we heard, "Battalion 15 to Englewood. Send in OFI." We looked at each other, and Tony called Englewood and told them that 464 was responding. Upon our arrival on the scene, we met Chief Marty Gawenda of the Fifteenth Battalion, on the outside of the structure.

Chief Gawenda informed us that there were at least three points of origin where fires were ignited in the building. He also said, "Cos, you will need your boots, because the sprinkler system has heads off throughout the structure."

As we entered the side door, water was flowing down about three stairs that led into a large open factory. Engine 65 had a one-and-three-quarter-inch hose line on what looked like cotton that was piled three feet high across this large area that was filled with smoke.

"Hey, Cos," Mike Hill yelled, "thanks for coming." Mike was on Truck 15 with me and we have been good friends for years. As he approached us, he was saying you don't have to be a rocket scientist to know that this one is arson. This guy started fires everywhere in this place.

Chief Gawenda also informed us that Truck Company 52 made a forced entry through this side entrance door, and all other entrances were locked. The fires were now all extinguished and Truck 52 had shut down the sprinkler system. Chief Gawenda said, "Cos if you don't need us for anything, we are going to return to quarters."

As we continued our scene investigation, we noted an odor similar in smell to a flammable throughout the first floor of this factory. Other than the main work area where there had been several bales of cotton type materials, we found two set fires at work tables in the center of the structure. There were two pallets next to a freight elevator that had been burned. In all, most of the fire was extinguished by the sprinkler system and then by the firefighters' line. Tony called me over to a closet under a stairwell that led up to the second floor. There was another fire in the closet. Then we found another point of origin in a section at the north end of the structure, under a phone distribution panel.

We knew that this was an arson for sure, and we must get the Chicago Police Department to secure this crime scene. We went back out the side door to tell the police officer that this is a crime

Plastic containers fill with flammable/combustibles in second floor office. Note: news paper rolled up in handle.

scene, but he was gone. He left when Engine 65 and Truck 52 returned to quarters!

I called the Englewood Fire Alarm Office on the portable radio and requested the police to return to the scene. Tony went back to the red and black sedan to get the camera and film. We started documenting each point of origin by photographing each of the multiple fires, and I made a small sketch of each area.

We found five points on the first floor, but Tony found a small fire at the bottom of a wooden stairway leading to the second floor. The stairs were wet from the sprinkler system, but the water was beading and was slippery. As we ascended to the second floor, there was a strong odor similar in smell to kerosene. We entered a workroom on the second floor that had many sewing machines and work areas with tables. On the wooden floor through this long room was a neat, clean, unburned trailer of flammable liquid that led into an office.

Inside this office, there were three five-gallon plastic containers filled with what appeared to be kerosene, and on the top of one container was an unburned paper, rolled up into the handle with newspapers all over the area. Tony said, "This guy didn't just want to start a fire, he wanted to blow this fucking place up." Just then I heard someone call to us. It was a Chicago police Officer named Burns. He asked what was going on. We explained to him what we had, and told him that he would probably need to call the Bomb and Arson section and get some detectives to respond immediately! Also, he should find out who owns the company and tell him to get his ass over here right away!

I guess I was a little hard on Officer Burns, but this isn't the first time that I have been left at a fire scene by the Chicago police. This is not a big fire for a firefighter, but it is a big deal for me, because I have been waiting to use all this training and schooling that I have been working on for the past year to catch an arsonist.

Tony called me over to the center of the building. He found the sprinkler room. "How could a guy be so fucking stupid not to shut down the sprinkler system before he starts the fire?" Tony said, as he photographed the room. We interviewed the vice president of the company. He said he had no idea of who would have started the fires, but he informed us that they had to lay off twenty-two employees this afternoon. This lay off happened each year at this time. It was normal procedure, but some of the people were angry. He also told us that there were only a few people working, and everyone left at about noon time. The owner and I locked up shortly afterwards and went home.

Tony and I left the scene in the custody of Officer Burns, who helped us out a lot. It was after nine o'clock by the time we got back to the firehouse.

Our job was done. We documented all the fires and determined the incident to be incendiary and the rest was up to the police. We ended the year of 1988 with 2,293 fire investigations that the Office of Fire Investigation responded to throughout the year.

One of the best things about closing out 1988 was that not one firefighter in Chicago died in the line of duty. It was a great year for me, because not only did I get my knowledge from attending all those classes, but I was able to apply this knowledge into the very fires I was responding to throughout Chicago. This training and my experience as a seasoned firefighter went together like pie and coffee.

It seemed that I met someone new every workday, because I am north, south, and on the west sides of this town every day. It could be in a hallway filled with smoke, or outside on the street. Most guys, firefighters, captains, lieutenants, and chiefs got to know me and knew I wasn't afraid to pick up a line or just help pulling a line. The first thing I did when I arrived in front of the building was to get any information I could from the first responding chief. Then I entered the building and followed the hose lines to the fire floor to see what was burning. That's how I have always done it since I got on this job.

The new year of 1989 came in very cold with temperatures reaching five degrees below zero and colder for the first week of this new year. It was cold, but not cold like we had in 1982. January 10, 1982 was the coldest day in Chicago's history when the temperature plummeted to twenty-six degrees below zero and a gusting thirty-five mile per hour wind that caused the wind chill factor to reach a numbing cold of eighty-one degrees below zero!

To be a firefighter that winter in 1982 was a bitch, to say the least. Within twenty-four hours there were some 350 incidents including seven multiple alarm fires. One fire I won't ever forget was when Engine 78 got a still at 720 North Juneway Terrace. It is very near the lake on the north side of Chicago. They reported fire on two floors and Battalion Twenty requested a box alarm. The weather situation was gusting winds off of Lake Michigan at thirty miles per hour and the temperature is sixteen degrees below zero. The fight was on! Within fifteen minutes, the Twentieth Battalion requested a "2-11" alarm fire. The request was refused because there were no more companies available for this fire. Things were so bad, they called the second shift in to relieve their worn out comrades. Suburban firefighters would respond to many extra alarms within the city. Eighteen suburbs sent equipment and firefighters to help us out. They loved it!

January 11, 1989 the first platoon was being relieved. We had gone through another busy twenty-four hours in OFI. The month of January has come in with a bang. Extra alarm fires every day. It was cold and snowing outside, as I warmed up my car in the lot in back of the firehouse. Carl Hopkins and Mike Cucci took my fire clothes out of the red and black sedan and put their fire gear in 464. Carl yelled, "We are in service, Cos, if you want to get going home." I looked at the clock and said, "Yeah, I'm going home for a long winter's nap like a fucking bear!

In that very early morning while I was in my sack, Engines 113, 77, Trucks 26, 14, Squad 1 and Battalion Thirteen responded to a still alarm at 4553 West Lexington Street.

Upon their arrival on the scene, battalion chief Tom O'Donnell reported smoke emanating from the service door on the west end of the north wall. Both engines are led out. The trucks are all working, and we have a good working fire. "Battalion Thirteen to Main. Give us a box," O'Donnell said. The structure involved was of mixed construction consisting of a trussed roof, one-story brick and a four-story brick mill construction. Alongside that were two concrete grain storage structures that were 70 and 80 feet high.

The fire has now extended westward through the supported

breach in the masonry wall the connects the two structures. A 2-11 alarm was requested and five more engines and two more truck companies responded to the 2-11 alarm. Hose lines are being stretched from engines to snorkels and tower ladders. 2-1-14 Joyce arrived at the scene. After a cursory look at the fire, he requested a 3-11 alarm. Chief Joyce was now concerned about getting the tower ladder in place on Lexington, or even moving it up on the expressway if possible.

Along with Chief Joyce was Commander Richard Kelly, a Chicago Fire Department Safety Officer. The two turned into the one-story section of the structure and were traveling north. Outside on Lexington, Carl Hopkins was interviewing a witness and out of the corner of his eye, the east wall of the four-story building came out and then fell in a split second so hard that when it hit, the ground shook all the way across Lexington Avenue! The wall fell onto the roof of the building that Chief Joyce and Commander Kelly just entered.

Stunned out of his mind, Dick Kelly started yelling and Joyce looked over and saw his helmet and then he saw some blood. Joyce remained calm, while Dick Kelly kept yelling. Joyce told Kelly it will be all right, just get some of these boards off me and grab me by my fire coat and lift me out.

Kelly started pulling the boards while Chief Joyce assessed the damage. His foot was pointing the opposite direction from his body. Kelly reached down and grabbed Joyce's fire coat to lift him and instantly, Joyce let out a yell with excruciating pain. He now knew he was in serious trouble! He somehow was able to pull his radio up to his mouth and yell, "Emergency, emergency to Main, the building fell in and we are trapped." Englewood answered, "Who's calling an emergency?" Joyce in a calm voice said, "2-1-14 to Englewood, I am trapped inside this building."

Within seconds firefighters from Truck 26 reached the district chief. A backboard was brought in. Chief Joyce was ever so carefully placed on the board. He was face down because of his back injury. They transferred Joyce to the stretcher and then to Ambulance 10.

After a short discussion, one paramedic said Northwestern has the Midwest Spinal Unit. Joyce looked over and said, "Northwestern." The ambulance ride was longer, but with some special escorts they were there in no time. The ride was still very hard on Chief Joyce and I'm sure he felt every bump on the way. The fire raged on for a few more hours and it was late afternoon by the time the still companies returned to quarters. But the search began for a cause of this fire right away. In an interview, a witness told Carl Hopkins that this girl, "Cheryl," came charging into this store and was outraged about her husband, who was fooling around with this other girl.

Mrs. Ellingham continued, "I was afraid of her, so I went over to Jim's Tire Service. When I returned, smoke was coming out that bedroom door, but Cheryl was gone. Then I called 9-1-1 from Jim's Tire Service."

Bomb and Arson Detective John Schmitz, in an interview, found out "Cheryl" called her sister-in-law and told her that she was going to burn his clothes by his dirty bed. The point of origin was located inside a small partitioned room that someone has been using as a bedroom. The fire originated in a pile of clothing on the floor, approximately three feet from the west exterior wall. Chicago Police Bomb and Arson Detective John Schmitz took the evidence. Some remnants of burned clothing were recovered as physical evidence.

The word went out fast that two firefighters were injured at this West Side blaze. Commander Kelly, a Chicago Fire Department Safety Officer, was taken to Loyola Hospital with cuts to his face and a possible skull fracture. Preliminary reports of injuries to James Joyce, District Chief of the Fourth District were cuts to his face, broken right ankle, broken left shoulder, and a possible broken back. Chief Joyce also sustained second- and third-degree burns to right side of his trunk.

In the early afternoon that same day of the fire, Detective John Schmitz of the Bomb and Arson section picked up the woman who allegedly started the fire. She was somewhere on North Keeler Avenue. He transported her to Eleventh and State, where Bomb and Arson detectives were headquartered.

She was carefully questioned, because it is a rule of law with regard to arson that every fire is presumed to be of accidental origin, and in order to establish arson, this presumption of an accidental ignition has to be overcome. So after a thorough fire scene examination and the elimination of all accidental and natural causal factors, this fire was the result of a willful act of incendiarism by this woman who utilized a handheld open flame ignition source, and deliberately ignited the available class A combustibles (clothing). She was arrested on two counts of arson, and two counts of aggravated arson. Assistant States Attorney Joanne Roddy took the suspect's statement.

The next day, Peg called me over to her area in the corner next to Chief Alletto's office. Peg told me that the Cook County Assistant States Attorney Diane Gordon called for me yesterday, and asked if I could call her today. "Thanks Peg," I said.

I was getting my coffee and wondering what fire she wanted to talk about. OFI has worked with the State Attorney's office on many occasions. However, when Diane Gordon calls, she usually has something of interest to say. Diane answered the phone and told me that I had a fire just before Thanksgiving where a one-year-old died in a CHA building on South Federal. "Sure," I said.

We talked about the fire for a few minutes. She is very thorough with her questions. She is a trial lawyer, who works very hard to prosecute the people who set fires. When all the of the concerned departments do their job, everything works well, but there are always objects in the way.

"We think we can get the mother on child endangerment because she didn't set the fire and we need to talk to you about it," Diane said.

I set a date for the next workday to meet with Diane Gordon in her office at Twenty-sixth and California to talk about the fire in the CHA high rise.

As I hung up the phone, Matt came into the kitchen to inform us about what we know about the 3-11 alarm fire on West Lexington, where Jim Joyce was injured the other day. I can't believe that this fire was caused by some woman who was jealous of her husband, and she ignited clothing that was inside a room that was a makeshift bedroom in a factory! Bomb and Arson detectives interviewed the husband, the girlfriend, and the fire setter. They charged her with aggravated arson. But so what? She will probably get off saying she was insane and how do you think Chief Joyce will feel hearing that the fire was the result of a goddamn love triangle!

You could see the anger in Captain Matt Moran's face as he explained the details of this fire. The motive she had is "revenge" against her husband and his lover. This type of fire setter is the worst, Matt said, because they don't care what happens. They just want some way to get even with the person who allegedly offended them. They are the most dangerous types of arson fires, but usually the easiest to solve.

I believe that all fire setters are potential murderers. In these cases, the arsonist is usually reacting in an extreme emotional state. This type might as well have a loaded gun, because there is a mixture of anger and retaliation, and they will do anything to get even. "We will see what happens in the courtroom when she is arraigned," Matt said. You could see in Matt's eyes that this fire was senseless, a "love triangle," and Matt Moran was mad that a chief officer was critically injured as a result.

Chapter 7

THE MONTH OF JANUARY HAS BEEN TOUGH ON FIREFIGHTERS AND THE equipment. We have had about 180 fire runs so far this month and of those fires, sixty-six have been still and box alarms, and also many extra alarm fires.

On January 31, we were back on duty, and there were a lot of things to take care of. The day shift had about ten follow-up investigations. Jack Lumsden was on a Daley day and he asked me if I could pick up ten cases of pop for our pop machine and also coffee and some other supplies. After I checked out the red and black sedan, and completed all the housework, Tony and I went for fuel at Eleventh and State. Then we went on our errands for Jack, to take care of the marshals' coffee and pop needs.

Finally, after a long and cold month, the temperature was supposed to hit the fifty-degree mark. The January thaw is here, thank God!

In Engine 61's firehouse, the firefighters had just finished the housework when the speaker opened. "Engines 61 and 50, Trucks 37 and 15, and the Seventeenth Battalion, you have a fire," the fire alarm operator said. It was 0959, the address was 5323 South Federal Street. "It's probably an incinerator," Jim Kuknyo said. He was on a traded-off day with Mike Gallapo.

Engine 61 reported on the scene and told the Englewood Fire Alarm Office that they have smoke emanating from windows on the fourth floor. The Alarm Office said, "Sixty-one you have smoke showing, Battalion Seventeen, you're now getting the Nineteenth Battalion and also Squad 5 to your fire." Tony Maritato looked over at me and I said, "It's the projects. It's probably an incinerator." We were at about Thirty-First and Halsted. The next voice we heard was Chief Harold Caponera. "Battalion Seventeen to Englewood. We have a little smoke on the fourth-floor end apartment. You can hold up that second Battalion Chief and Squad 5," the chief said.

Within minutes of that radio transmission, Chief Harold Caponera yelled, "Emergency, give us a box." I turned the sedan around so fast that Tony fell against the passenger door, and said "What the fuck are you doing"? Caponera never yells like that, something is wrong," I said. "Tell the office that 4-6-3 is taking in the still and box." Looking south on the Dan Ryan Expressway, you could see black smoke rising from the row of Robert Taylor housing projects that lined the east side of the expressway.

Again in a very excited voice, "Battalion 17 to Englewood. Give me an EMS Plan 2. I have injured firefighters," the chief said. An EMS Plan 2 is ten ambulances. "What happened?" I thought to myself. By the time I arrived on the scene of the fire and Truck 15 had moved their rig up between the sixteen-story buildings, they had their main ladder raised up to the fourth floor. Most of the fire had been extinguished by now, but smoke and steam continued to roll out of the windows. I met Chief Caponera. He said, "Cos, it just blew on us." You could see the agony in his face as he said, "They all jumped out the window." This was a fire chief who had come up through the ranks and had seen a lot of fire duty.

I tried to console him, but he was just too distraught. As I looked over to the base of the building, firefighters and paramedics were collecting an MSA mask that had been lying on the muddy ground. In a parking lot just to the south of the fire building were ambulances that had taken the injured firefighters and were about to leave for the hospitals.

I needed to know what happened, as I looked up to see the scorch marks on the beige bricks above the fourth-floor windows. There was a fire helmet and some other items on the hood of the Seventeenth Battalion's red and black sedan. There was a shiny type of melted material on the helmet of one of the firefighters. I thought to myself, "What is that?" Lieutenant John (Red) Finn was just standing next to the chief's car. I asked him if he was all right and he just kept staring like he didn't know me. "What happened?" I asked. He said "We were using hand pumps waiting for a line and bang! the whole fucking place lit up." I looked at the back of his head. His hair was burned and so was the back of his ears. He was in shock and dazed. The paramedics helped him into the back of Ambulance 8 and I walked toward the building.

So far, I didn't know anything about what happened. I started following two two-and-a-half-inch hose lines up to the fourth floor. That has already told me that a conventional lead out in a structure with a standpipe is wrong.

When I arrived on the fourth floor, the first person I met was Lieutenant Lee Rodak of Engine 61. He was truly shaken. He informed me that they knew they had a fire. "We went up with the hand pumps and hose that they hooked up to the wall hydrant, but when the Engineer sent the water, all the fittings on the lower floors were off, and water was shooting out all over the fucking place! I ordered a conventional lead out, but that would take time. In the meantime, we used hand pumps." Lee said he went to the apartment entrance door to call for more hand pumps, and also to see how the lead out of the hose was going. "All of a sudden, I heard and felt this rumbling sound, and a boom. The whole apartment lit up with a tremendous amount of fire."

George Hensley is a firefighter I had worked with on Cottage Grove. He was now on Engine 61 and he said they all just jumped out the windows. "When it blew, they just jumped," he repeated over and over. He was dazed and confused and you could see it in his face.

There were about twenty firefighters working in apartment 401. They were overhauling what was left to the contents of this three-bedroom apartment, and the room was still hot.

Lieutenant Rodak told me that the fire was in the southwest bedroom just inside the door. There were plenty of firefighters, so the chief ordered any of the guys from Engine 61 to the ground floor.

I interviewed a woman, Mrs. Williams, who was the occupant of apartment 401, and she also was the person who discovered the fire. She stated that at the time, she was in the front bedroom lying on the bed with her children, when she heard some type of popping sounds and also smelled smoke. Mrs. Williams further stated that she saw flames on the floor in a pile of clothing inside the bedroom in front of a wooden dresser.

Tony Maritato came upstairs, and told me that eight firemen had been taken to area hospitals and a few of them are in critical condition. "Cos," Tony said, "they had to jump out the fucking window on the fourth floor and landed on top of each other on the ground"!

I asked the occupant of apartment 415 if I could use her telephone. I called OFI and talked to Peggy for a second. She called Captain Moran and Chief Alletto, and I informed them of what I had. Matt said, "Marshal we will be there in ten minutes. Stay right there."

Two more guys from OFI showed up. Bob Villanueva and Joe Kinnerk. They asked us if we could use some help. I asked them if they could find out the names of all the firemen who were injured and what hospitals they were transported to. Tony and I returned to the burned-out apartment 401. From what we heard, it blew with rumbling and explosions. I knew something very bad had happened. These firefighters, Jim Kuknyo and Joe Gaska were seasoned firemen and were in a thousand fires in the projects. But why was this one so bad that it made them jump out the fourth-floor window. Was there a flammable combustible type of material that ignited?

Chief Alletto and Captain Moran arrived at the burned-out apartment, and I was glad to see them. We looked through what was left of the contents and followed the burn patterns.

We had the Chicago Fire Department Photo Unit take pictures of the interior and exterior of the structure. There were no signs of a flammable liquid, and we eliminated the cooking stove. Matt and I interviewed the occupant, Mrs. Williams. She said the fire was in a pile of clothing on the floor in the front bedroom and she heard a popping sound behind the bedroom door.

We cleared away all the debris on the floor along what was a partition wall. There were the remains of an electrical cord that was plugged into a duplex electrical outlet that was about six inches from floor level. This outlet showed excessive heat stress and literally crumbled when we started to inspect it, along with the "1900" electrical box that the outlet was affixed to.

With all the tools that we carry, we started to examine all the other duplex outlets in the bedroom. This was the only outlet that showed any heat stress. There were also two blades that we found leading to the wire. The blades were the remains of what was a lamp plug at the end of the cord. The pieces were fitting together. Matt said, "This was some type of short circuit right here." We photographed the evidence, and collected the remains of the cord and the duplex outlet.

"But what about the explosion? They all said it blew." Matt said, "We will work that out when we get back to the firehouse." In the meantime, the press was outside with cameras in hand. "So Marshals, hush is the word," Matt said. "Don't tell anyone shit! In fact, don't even tell Chief Kehoe or any of the firefighters until we get this all straightened out. Okay? You guys check out the firefighters that were taken to Mercy Hospital. They were L. C. Merrell of Truck 37, and Tylie McShane of Truck 16. Then go over to Michael Reese Hospital to see how Firefighter Joe Gaska from Engine 50 is doing, and we will all meet back at 1401 South Michigan."

As we came down from the burned-out apartment, and Matt said "Hush is the word," Chief Alletto went out on the Federal side of the building and Tony and I left through the front on State Street. All of a sudden the press had us completely surrounded. Asking all types of questions, we told them that it was still under investigation and we have no comment! Chief Kehoe said, "Well what have we got?" I said, "Nothing so far Chief. We will call you later."

We interviewed Tylie McShane and L. C. Merrell, the two firefighters from Truck 37. They both had first and second-degree burns to the face and neck. They stated that they were in the hall with hand pumps. The smoke was heavy and all of a sudden the heat came and there was fire everywhere.

At Michael Reese Hospital, we interviewed Joseph Gaska from Engine 50. We had known each other for years. He was in a lot of pain, but he told me that they had no water in their line and were using hand pumps. "As Jim Kuknyo and I were changing positions, the window in the bedroom broke and the whole place just exploded into flames." With agony in his face he continued.

"Cos, we crawled into the next room, but there was fire all over our heads. We made it to the window. There were no choices. We were starting to burn and we had to jump." The doctors came in and said Mr. Gaska was going to surgery. I felt so bad for Joe Gaska. He had burns to his face, neck, hands, multiple broken bones, and possible spinal injuries. On the first floor of Michael Reese Hospital, the press was everywhere. An aide to the fire commissioner told me that the commissioner wanted to talk to me. Fire Commissioner Louis Galante was off to one side as I approached him.

I was introduced and he said, "Okay, what happened over there." I hesitated for a second and thought about what Matt said (hush is the word). I told the commissioner that I could not tell him anything yet, because Chief Alletto said not to tell anyone.

With a smile or a grin on his face, the commissioner said, "Come over here, son." He pulled me away from the press into a small room. He looked me right in the eye and said, "I admire your dedication and loyalty to Chief Alletto and the job," and then in a loud voice he added, "I am the fucking fire commissioner and you are going to tell me what happened at that fire today!" I proceeded to tell him everything that I knew about the electrical outlet, and that there were no standpipes in service, and about the hand pumps. By the time we returned to the firehouse, it was just past 1400 hours.

Matt walked up to me and said, "What did I tell you? Hush is the word, right?" In my defense I said, "But he is the fire commissioner." Matt said, "I don't care, you spilled the beans, Marshal." Then I said, "He is the commissioner," and Matt started laughing. He was breaking my balls, and then we all started laughing. I guess I needed something to cheer me up after a very sad day.

That night I went to Little Company of Mary Hospital to visit with my good friend Jim Kuknyo. He was in intensive care with a broken right ankle, broken left leg, extreme back pain (possible vertebrae damage), possible pelvic fracture, and abrasions to his face and arms.

From our fire scene examination, it appeared that this fire was caused by an electrical malfunction. As a result of the stand-pipe being out of service, the time it took to make a conventional hose lead out took a longer time. Heavy smoke concentrations cause a build up of carbon monoxide and high temperatures between 1200 degrees and 1400 degrees. From this build up, the window glass in the southwest bedroom began to lose its shape and compromise. This thermal stress caused the window to crack and fall toward the heat source. The large concentrations of oxygenated air caused the carbon monoxide within the super heated air to ignite rapidly and caused the apartment to explode into a heavy volume of fire. Carbon monoxide has an ignition temperature of 1128 degrees. This fire was what firefighters call a "backdraft." Its flammable or explosive limits are between 12.5 to 74 with a vapor density of 1.0.

Firefighting has become increasingly complex and dangerous. Despite the constant improvements of protective clothing and self-contained breathing equipment, always remember that the job of firefighting still remains a very dangerous profession.

The injuries to Chief Jim Joyce, James Kuknyo, John (Red) Finn, Joseph Gaska, Dennis Harris, Freeman Gilbert, Tylie McShane, and L. C. Merrell, will always be remembered as one of the worst January months on record where firefighters in Chicago paid a big price.

I have lived in a new neighborhood on Chicago's South Side for a few years now. It is called "Talley's Corner," and is located on the north end of Mount Greenwood. It is home to many Chicago police officers and firefighters. One day a guy knocked on my door and introduced himself as my precinct captain. After a short conversation, I found out that he lived a few miles away from this neighborhood. I thought how can this guy represent me and my new neighborhood if he doesn't even live here? I called a long time friend Ed Maloney, whom I went to grammar school with.

Ed was a precinct captain in his own neighborhood in the Nineteenth Ward. I asked Ed how this guy could be the precinct captain and how can he care about the interests of the people in Talley's Corner?

Within the next week, Ed Maloney called me back and asked me to attend a meeting at the Nineteenth Ward office. At this meeting I was asked by Thomas Hynes, the Ward Committeeman, if I wanted to become the new precinct captain of the new Seventy-fifth Precinct. I was flattered by the offer from Tom Hynes and accepted the position.

It was also a great opportunity for me to work with another good friend, Michael Sheehan, who was the Alderman of the Nineteenth Ward. Mike Sheehan and Ed Maloney and I had gone to the same grammar school, Saint Cajetan. I think Mike Sheehan was also best known as the only Big Ten Referee on the city council. He served as chairman of the council's Police, Fire, and Municipal Institutions Committee. With much encouragement from my friends, I now became the precinct captain of Talley's Corner, Brother Rice High School, Mother McAuley High School, and Saint Xavier College.

With a new election not more than a month away, Local 2 was the very first public employee union to endorse Richard M. Daley for mayor.

The time before the 1989 special mayoral election was very exciting for me. A firefighter who was given a chance to see the ins and outs of Chicago politics right in my own backyard! As the election tallies came in on April 4, 1989, Richard M. Daley was elected mayor of Chicago. The time has come to make the firefighters morale our first priority. We have the best ever contract in place. The remaining two-and-one-half years we will get increases in our wages of 4.5 percent and in 1991 we will get a 7 percent raise in pay.

The old timers are the ones who laid the groundwork for today's firefighter and we still should be grateful for all their sacrifices. If they could only see the manpower and the benefits we receive today. Mayor Daley did not waste any time and after Fire Commissioner Louis Galante "retired," he appointed Raymond Orozco as the new fire commissioner.

On June 16, 1989 Commissioner Orozco appointed Chief Alletto Director of Fire Investigation to Deputy Fire Commissioner of Support Services. I was happy for Chief Alletto. I was also upset because I would not have access to his fire investigation expertise as readily as I had before. However, Commissioner Orozco, in his wisdom, had OFI placed under the administration control of the Bureau of Support Services, so that Chief Alletto could oversee the OFI operation.

One of the first things that happened under this new administration was the cut of manpower in OFI. Over twenty investigators were returned to firefighting duties on fire companies. Chief Pat Burns was now in charge of the Office of Fire Investigation, and instead of four or five marshals working every day, there were only two marshals, or sometimes one! Naturally Chief Alletto was not happy about this and said so to Commissioner Orozco. Chief Alletto was never bashful when he had something important to say!

Matt said, "From now on, you take the fire, but if you can't finish the report, take care of it when you can. This working by yourself stinks and its dangerous. Don't take any chances. If there are no police on the scene, then call the Fire Alarm Office and request a car. Don't get hurt, Marshals, we can't afford any lay-ups now."

Mike Deckelmann worked the day shift with Matt and Tom Purdy. Purdy took care of the administrative and the paperwork with Peggy. Deckelmann did most of the follow-up investigations that we classified undetermined, and also responded to fires if the two cars were at fire scenes and unavailable.

The fires did not slow down and in fact, we were now going to more fires! In the early afternoon, a fire was given to Engine companies 59 and 83 and Truck companies 47 and 22 to a still and box alarm at 4727 North Malden. Upon their arrival on the scene, there was a heavy smoke and fire condition and fire was noted issuing from the third-floor windows on the north side of the subject structure.

The physical description of the fire building was a four-story brick apartment building, which contained eighty rental units, of which sixty were occupied. Battalion Nine requested a 2-11 alarm and EMS Plan 1. Truck 47 threw their main ladder to rescue victims from the third and fourth floors. Ground ladders were raised by firefighters of Truck Company 22 in both the front and rear of the structure.

Engine 83 lead out a two-and-a-half-inch line to the third floor, and Engine 59 lead out two lines through the side door on the north end of the structure. People were screaming for help. Paramedics from Ambulance 13 and 40 were carrying victims from the fire scene toward their ambulances.

The area of origin was located in a hallway at the north end. Firefighters from Engine 59 battled the flames and were able to enter the apartments. Once they entered apartment 304, they found the body of a woman just inside the apartment door. As they continued extinguishing the fire, they found the bodies of two men in a bathroom. When the battle was over, ten people were injured and three people were dead.

After a thorough fire scene examination of the area, it was determined that the heaviest burning took place at the north end of a hall in front of apartment 304. The apartment door had very even deep charring and the wood trim was burned almost completely off. At the base of the door frame were the springs of a mattress. There were indications that the mattress was leaning against the wall when it was burning.

In an interview with the tenant of apartment 326, he stated that the mattress was leaning against the wall for a few days. He further stated that he left his apartment to go to the store about ten minutes before, and there was no smoke or fire in the hallway.

Bomb and Arson detectives interviewed the tenants in apartment 307. They said that there was an argument going on just before the fire, with the tenant of apartment 310, who had been taken to Weiss Hospital. The three bodies of the victims were taken to Illinois Masonic Hospital and pronounced DOA by a Dr. Kim. The fire was struck out and all the fire companies were returning. I was by myself now, that there were only two marshals working after the cut in manpower.

Bomb and Arson detectives O'Meara and Schmitz returned to the scene from Weiss Hospital and informed me that the woman from apartment 310 confessed to setting the mattress on fire with an open flame. Her reason was that three people in apartment 304 had drunk all her wine when she went for a pack of cigarettes.

We all returned to the third floor to photograph the mattress and the door. The detectives collected evidence from the scene and the woman was charged with four counts of aggravated arson.

As I was returning to quarters, all I could think about was

two Chicago firefighters were injured and three people were dead all because of her fucking wine! The firehouse was dark when I returned. Louis Outlaw had a fire on the West Side with Engine Company 99. Here I am with a big fire story to tell about aggravated arson and no one to tell it to. There is something creepy about being in a firehouse all by yourself. I finished my report and went to bed. Next workday, I will have to go over to the Cook County Morgue to get the names of the three victims from the fire on Malden, and the official cause of death.

We have a new address for Chicago Firefighters' Union Hall. It is located at 440 West Forty-third Street. Our Union Local 2 has come a long way in such a short time. Because we can remember, not so long ago, a union that was financially struggling after the 1980 Union Strike against the city of Chicago. Local 2 is now on a strong financial base again, because of the good judgment of our elected officers, especially Billy McGrane, the secretary-treasurer. He did an outstanding job over the years. He knows how to manage the union's funds.

President Marty O. Holland likes to call them the twenty-year dreams because it took twenty years to get the 50/20 bill passed, but we did it! It took twenty long years to end the widows poverty pension, but we did it! It took twenty years to get collective bargaining, but we did it! The next twenty-year dream was to purchase our own union building, and we now have our own building! Why pay rent when you can build equity in something that you own.

The next workday I relieved the third platoon, which was two guys. The lieutenant, Wally Burke, met me at the door and asked, "Are you ready to go into service, Cos?"

I said, "Sure, Marshal, why?"

He said, "You got a fire in the Third Battalion. They just called."

"Were you banking this one?"

"Yeah, just a little, because I am going golfing this morning."
Wally removed his fire clothes from 463 and I threw my gear in
the back seat of the sedan. "Oh, by the way, Jack Lumsden called
in last night and he's laid up with a bad back. You will be working alone today, Marshal!"

"That's just fucking great," I said.

I pulled out of the firehouse with my lights and siren on.
Working the whole city of Chicago by myself. Battalion Three
was waiting on North Ashland Avenue. The fire was out, and
Engine 30 was picking up their hose from the street when I
arrived on the scene. The fire originated under a wooden exteri-
or porch in the rear of the building and the cause ended up being
an electrical malfunction in a light fixture. Engine 30 was returning to their quarters and asked me if I wanted to stop for coffee.

I told them I needed to get some information from the owner,
and also exchange times and numbers with the beat cop. "But
thanks anyway for the offer, guys."

After finishing up with the police about this accidental fire, I
started back to the firehouse. All I can think about is, I will be the
only car working today, and somehow this is wrong. Captain
Moran met me at the door as I was backing into the firehouse. He
told me that Jack Lumsden had a pinched nerve in his neck, and
will be laid up for a few days. He said, "If you are at a fire and
need any help, call me. I don't care what time it is, I will
respond." I thanked Matt and I knew he was worried, because he
usually jokes around. But not today. He had a look of worry and
aggravation on his usually smiling face.

I left the firehouse and went over to the Cook County
Morgue on West Harrison Street to get the names and ages of the
three people who died in the fire on Malden the other day. I
arrived at the morgue at 1000 and told the person in the front

office that I was a fire marshal from the Office of Fire Investigation.

I was introduced to a Mr. Roy Dames, who is the executive director of the Cook County Medical Examiner's Office. As he led me down a long hall, Roy said that I looked like a very good friend of his, a fishing partner. He said his name is Jack Adams, and I stopped walking for a second. "Jack is my cousin, and he is also one of my fishing partners." We both laughed as we continued through a set of double doors. Roy picked up a clipboard and said only one of the three people had been identified. The other two were still listed as John Doe's. As he continued, we went through another set of doors, and across a dock area. There were stainless steel tables with large wheels lined up against the wall. We went through some heavy clear acrylic curtains. Inside were the bodies of people who were brought into the morgue in the last couple of days. As Roy and Mike Boehmer moved the tables back and over to the side, he said, "Here are your fire victims from the fire on Malden."

The lifeless bodies of two black men under the fluorescent lighting looked so different from how they looked at the fire scene.

As we were walking out of this cold building, you could see the shelves that went up over ten feet high with bodies on many of them. I was relieved to be back in the dock area where a funeral director in his pinstriped suit pants said to Roy, "How long is this going to take?"

Roy looked at him and said, "Mike, it will take as long as it takes. But we will have all the information right." The funeral director was pacing back and forth like a distraught kid and saying, "I'll never be ready." Roy looked at him again and said, "I really feel sorry for you, Mike. You only have four funerals today," and laughed as we walked away. Roy asked me if I wanted some coffee, but I declined and said there was a fire in the Roseland area, and Engine 62 was leading out hose. I told Roy about the cut in manpower in OFI and that I was the only guy working today. He said, "For the whole city?" "Yeah, the whole city for the next twenty-one hours." I shook his hand and walked outside. It was eighty-four degrees, but it felt good to be out of that building.

I made my way back to 1401 South Michigan. Peggy was the only one in the firehouse when I returned. She told me that Chief Burns and Captain Moran were at a meeting at city hall with Chief Alletto. Peggy said if it wasn't just to answer the phones, they could have let her go also. Now with all the fire marshals gone she had hardly any typing, and it was a little scary to be alone in the firehouse.

I walked into the kitchen. Not only was it empty, but it was filthy. There were dishes and coffee cups stacked in the sink. The garbage was overflowing and even though we didn't have a cooking club, guys still used the stove and left a greasy frying pan. I opened the journal on the desk and found a note from Lieutenant Wally Burke. "Cos, sorry for the mess, but we had seven fires yesterday. P.S., thanks for taking the run this morning." There also was a note from Matt. "Marshal, you are the acting lieutenant today. Make sure your men clean the kitchen and bunk room, ha ha." Even with the mess and my anger about working alone, Matt's humor made me feel better.

I filled out the roll call (just me) in the journal and entered my first run of the day. While I was making the coffee, the red phone (marshal line) rang.

"Cosgrove, this is the Main Fire Alarm Office and the Eighth Battalion is requesting OFI at 1711 North Mayfield." I told the Main Fire Alarm Office that there was only one car working the whole city and that was me, 463. "Okay, Cos," the office said. The fire dispatcher then said, "Are you taking in the Eighth Battalion's fire?" I replied, "Yes sir, I'm on my way."

The fire was in a three-story brick apartment building, and upon the arrival of Engine Company 68 and Truck 53 there was fire issuing from the first-floor windows on the west side of the structure. Also, a man was found lying on the front lawn with burns to 90 percent of his body. After a thorough fire scene examination, the burn patterns revealed that this fire was the result of a very disgruntled man who poured gasoline on the stairway, igniting same with a hand held open flame, but was unable to get out before he was burned by his own fire! The victim was transported to Loyola Hospital in Maywood by the paramedics of Ambulance 15. By the time I left Loyola Hospital and returned to the firehouse it was after 1600. I never got a chance to talk to Chief Burns or Captain Moran that day. I ended up with five fire investigations by 1600!

With the recent cut in manpower, a rumor was out that the Office of Fire Investigation was going out of service. Another rumor was that the Chicago Police Bomb and Arson section was going to conduct all the fire investigations in Chicago.

Chief Alletto, upon hearing the rumors, almost went through the roof of city hall. He assured us that the Illinois State Statutes were mandated by the General Assembly as follows: "That a fire inspector of every municipality with a population of 500,000 or more shall investigate the cause, origin, and circumstances of every fire occurring in the municipality." This rumor was bullshit because OFI will not go out of service. However, we still had only one or two men per shift. The work was hard and Chief Alletto said we would get some of the marshals back in September, and to please be patient, as he was working hard to accomplish this task.

Chapter 8

I WAS GETTING A LOT BETTER AT MY REPORT WRITING AND SPELLING. Peggy would compliment me on occasion and I did appreciate the compliment. One afternoon Chief Burns called me into his office and told me that Assistant United States Attorney Patricia Holmes wanted to talk to me.

I said to Pat Burns, "For what? I didn't do anything!" Pat laughed and said, "No, no, Marshal, she wants to talk about a fire you had last year at 3729 South Saint Louis."

"Oh yeah, the arson fire in that factory."

Pat said, "Here's her number, give her a call." Patricia Holmes wanted to talk to me about being a witness. I set a date for the first week in September.

One afternoon Matt called me in his cubicle and said, "Marshal, do you know what a slumlord is?" Well I didn't really know, but what I heard is this is the owner of a building who lets the building get run down and just collects the rent.

Matt said, "That's right. There was another fire up in Engine 83's still district, a 2-11 alarm. Mike Schoenecker had the fire, but he turned it in as an undetermined. Sure enough, the owner is the same guy all the time, Louis Fox. He controls dozens of storefronts on Broadway and Sheridan Road. Many are lounges and strip joints. This guy owns and controls so much property in Chicago that he is known on a first name basis in building court."

Matt's desk was covered with paperwork of old Chicago Fire Department incident reports. Here were ten fires that OFI responded to. Most of them were up in the forty-eighth ward, and in this one, two firefighters were injured. Matt said that he met with the Alderman, Kathy Osterman about this guy. She said he has a strangle hold on her ward. The Alderman said that he destroys a neighborhood and they are powerless against him. His strategy is known as "land banking." He picks a piece of commercial or residential property that is in financial trouble because the owner blew the tax bill or his bank loan is in arrears.

Matt said, "Kathy Osterman is the forty-eighth ward alderman and she loves this ward. She was almost in tears when she told me that when this guy gets a building, it is doomed. He may lease it or just hold on to it, or wait for a buyer to come along with the right price. No one knows how much real estate he owns, but there are lists of properties under other names, and he makes extensive use of blind trusts. He usually pays for everything in cash, and runs a dozen companies that are not even listed in the phone book. Marshal, when I left Osterman's office I just wanted to somehow get this dog ass and bring him into court. He's no fucking good! A real money grabbing rat."

"Here is one fire on the West Side that we thought we had him on. It was a big vacant warehouse fire in Engine 77's district. The police caught a guy who was the torch and they got him to point the finger at this guy, Fox. But the conviction never stuck. The insurance company refused to pay his claim because we classified the fire as arson. He turned around and sued the insurance company for $415,000. Guess how much he paid for the building? $300,000! This sleazy prick knows how to make fucking money. This guy is making big bucks on the back of the poor people and firefighters."

I asked Matt "How do we find him?

"They say he has an office located in the back of some abandoned theater called 'Uptown.' We have been up there to visit him, but the only way into this theater is a rear stairway entrance. The rest of the building is boarded up. So, Marshal, if you get a fire up in the forty-eighth ward, make sure you document everything about the fire, because sooner or later this guy will make a mistake and just maybe you or I can get him. He is the scum of the earth and probably has caused injury and death to firemen."

I listened to Matt, because he has so much knowledge. Not only about the fire department, but a little about everything in general. Now that there are only a couple of us working every day, Matt would help me out with my reports and I was always asking him questions. If he didn't know the answer today he would tell me at our next meeting. I really never knew how much work he had to do himself, because he never showed me anything. But, because of the manpower situation in OFI, a lot of undetermined fires were piling up. Mike Deckelmann was taking all he could handle. Plus they were taking fires in from their homes at night. It was just crazy.

It became so crazy, that at one time, I was seven or eight fires behind. We never got any sleep because we were always writing. I often thought about going back to a fire company. If we had a fire you worked very hard putting it out, but then there was no writing. I said it before, but it bears saying again, "I love being a Chicago firefighter."

As much as I loved pulling ceilings, effecting ventilation, and all the other challenges of being a firefighter, I just could not go back to a fire company and give up all that I have learned about fire investigation. Just as I was on a fire company, I still get very excited on a daily basis to see what new and amazing moment will be around the next corner.

It didn't take long. The radio crackled, "Engine 63 on the scene, 6610 South Ellis, we got a two-story brick occupied, and we have a fire." A second later, "Battalion Seventeen to Englewood, we have a fire in a three-story brick about 50 by 75 feet, occupied, both engines are leading out." I knew better than to go to bed when Harold Caponera was out in the street. I looked up at the clock on the wall. It was 0215.

"Englewood, emergency, give us a box." "Okay Battalion Seventeen, you got a box," the office repeated. I started out the door of the firehouse and told the office that 463 was taking in the still and box on Ellis. Chief Caponera called for an ambulance and I knew that not only was someone hurt, but the firefighters are again in a battle. Engine 63 was pumping from the corner, the engineer was busy with the hose lines. We made contact with a small nod of our heads, and I continued toward the fire. The reflections of the spectacular flames that were issuing from the roof lit up the nighttime sky as I approached.

I met up with Chief Caponera. "How're we doing, Chief?" I asked.

"Cos, we got two people out the second floor. When we got here, there was fire blowing out the windows on the first floor in the rear. The ambulance went to Billings with the people."

"Okay Chief," I said.

As I entered the smoke-filled hallway on the first floor, a fireman was down on his knees coughing and choking, trying to get a breath of fresh air. Water was streaming from their fire hose cascading down the stairs and out onto the front lawn of this burning structure.

Around the back of the burning building were many more

firefighters attacking the fire, yelling back and forth to each other, as they ascended up the charred wooden back porches.

The Chicago police were interviewing the occupants, who were still dressed in night clothes and blankets. "There was a sound of breaking glass," one interviewee said, "and then a lot of smoke."

The tenant on the first floor was evicted yesterday by the landlord. We have a set fire I think. I was able to get into the kitchen of the first floor and you could smell an odor similar to gasoline. At about this time, the firefighters started to withdraw their lines. This fire is just about extinguished.

My fire incident scene investigation clearly indicated that this fire was no accident! The police had two people in the back seat of their car. One officer told me that the neighbor picked this guy out of the crowd. He said after hearing the glass break, he saw this guy running out toward the alley and he jumped the fence.

Bomb and Arson were responding. I told Chief Caponera what we had so far. "Cos, I knew when I arrived this was arson. A building doesn't have this much fire at 0200 in the morning." Harold Caponera had been fighting fires for a long time in this area.

The firefighters were all busy picking up their hoses and ladders. Although their faces were covered with soot and dirt, they still were able to joke about the meatloaf from dinner. It wasn't the smoke that made him throw up in the hallway, it was the meatloaf. Everyone started laughing.

Chief Caponera said, "Hey Cos, we're going home. Give me a call on the marshal line about the cause." "Okay boss," I said, as the rigs started to pull away. The fire was out, and now I needed to put the facts together about how this all occurred.

They took the suspects to the police station over at Fifty-first and Wentworth. Bomb and Arson detective Larry Gates said they reentered the structure and found pieces of a broken bottle right where the witness said the window was broken.

Gates took the piece of glass and some debris for evidence, and we traded some of our times and numbers related to the fire. We photographed the interior and exterior of the burned-out structure and I told Gates that I would meet him at the fifty-first and Wentworth police District.

The police station was filled with police officers coming and going. I told the cop at the desk who I was, and he showed me into the lock-up where the two guys were taken for questioning.

Detective Larry Gates told me that this guy in the first room lived in the first-floor apartment with his mother. The guy in the second room was just a friend, but he already ratted out the other guy, because we told him that he was going down for twenty years for arson. After that, he started singing like a fucking canary! It seems that Jimmy Wood and his mom were evicted from the first-floor apartment for lack of payment of rent. He was pissed off about this and filled up a large glass bottle with gasoline and threw it through the rear window of the first floor.

Detective Gates said, "Come into the interrogation room." Against the wall sitting on a three-foot bench was an angry young man. I sat down at a table across the room from him, and just stared at him. All of a sudden in a loud tone of voice he said, "What are you looking at, motherfucker!"

I did not answer him, I just stared at him.

"What are you looking at?" he said. I told him I was looking at a piece of shit that is handcuffed to a large steel ring. "Fuck you, what do you want?"

Gates said, "Mr. Woods, you have to be nice. This is a fire investigator from the Chicago Fire Department."

"What's he want with me?"

"I told you, I just need your name, address, and where you're going to be staying now that you burned your apartment."

"I didn't burn the motherfucking apartment," he said.

"Actually," I said, "I need to know why you made fifty-two firefighters and two paramedics wake up and take off their pajamas and put on all that heavy firefighting equipment and rescue four people, two of whom are now in Billings Hospital. That's why I am here, motherfucker," I yelled. "At four-thirty in the morning. That's why I am here."

He didn't say anything, and I just walked out the door. I told Gates that I would call him later. I stopped at Huck Finn's for donuts on the way back to the firehouse on Michigan Avenue. It was 0530. I made myself a pot of coffee and ate a donut and started another fire report. At around 0700, I called Chief Caponera to tell him that the cops would probably charge this kid with arson for burning up the apartment on Ellis.

Chief Caponera said, "Thanks Cos, and by the way, did you hear that Frank Connors is real sick? They think it's cancer, Cos, and it don't look good." After hanging up the phone I just sat there thinking about my good friend Frank Connors, whom I had the pleasure of working with on Engine 45 at forty-sixth and Cottage Grove for many years.

Soon Matt came in and said, "Marshal, you look like shit." "Thanks, I feel like shit too," I said and I told him about Frank Connors. Matt said, "Hey they are doing a lot with cancer today, and Frank is a strong guy. Hey, Marshal, here is some good news. After nine months of agonizing surgery, Chief Jim Joyce is coming back to work."

I was very surprised to hear the news about Jim Joyce. His injuries were so severe that everyone thought he would never return to the fire department. The burns that he sustained to the right side of his body were enough to put the average firefighter off the job, but not this guy. He's a tough prick, I thought to myself. After being admitted to Northwestern Hospital, his injuries included a broken left shoulder, a broken left ankle, and a fractured thoracic vertebrae in his back. His doctors were mostly concerned with the back injury. Joyce's doctors made a decision to operate on his back first, and then the shoulder. They would let him recover for a while and then rebreak his left ankle, and set it properly.

The shoulder had to heal in order to get him to use crutches, and start him in an extensive therapy program. Just one day short of three months in the hospital, on April 10 he returned home. After many months of physical therapy and mental anguish, this third-generation fireman had one thing on his mind, getting back to the Chicago Fire Department. He never thought his career was over. On September 16, 1989 Fire Commissioner Orozco appointed Jim Joyce to Deputy Fire Commissioner of the Bureau of Emergency Medical Services.

Although Jim Joyce probably would have wanted to go back into fire suppression and rescue, I am pretty sure he was just happy to be back to work, even if it meant commanding paramedics.

The fires kept coming, and the guys that were left in OFI were getting very tired of working alone. Finally we got some help. Chief Alletto told Pat Burns to start calling a few of the men back from fire companies, one on every shift. It was a lot better, but it was never the same.

In the late fall, we found out that firefighter Frank Connors had become ill with a sore throat. That was in August. He was laid up and went to see a doctor. They put him on antibiotics, but he just didn't get better. After returning to the doctor, he found what they called a lymphoma on Frank's neck. The doctor ordered a biopsy. It was determined that Frank had cancer. He underwent surgery for the removal of a malignant lymph node. Following this surgery, Frank began the very long and tiring chemotherapy treatments.

We as firefighters know that smoke is not good for us to inhale. If that shit was any good, they would have put it in bottles, and would sell it at the store.

Frank Connors worked in some of the busiest firehouses in the city of Chicago, and I know firsthand that he was an aggressive firefighter, and most often he was the first in a fire building. The fires that we fought were most often multiple dwellings and the smoke that was given off by the fire had high levels of vinyl chloride, which is found in plastics as well as many other carcinogens and toxins. It was a hostile environment to say the least, but none of us who really loved it would trade places with anyone!

Our method of protection in those days was to hold your breath, but we all know that did not work. As a result, you were subject to smoke and heat when you inhaled the toxic gases. While working at a fire you just breathed more deeply because the body requires a lot of oxygen.

There is a definite link between cancer and certain carcinogens such as vinyl chlorides and substances such as benzene and asbestos, which we undoubtedly came in contact with working at fires.

Our job is to extinguish the fire, and open the walls and ceilings in search of hidden fire. When we open the walls and ceiling, the asbestos becomes airborne. Asbestos fibers enter the body by inhalation and can become embedded in the tissues of the respiratory system. A cancerous tumor spreads rapidly in cells of membranes covering the lungs and other body organs. Generally, these symptoms do not show their ugly heads for some twenty years or more after the initial exposure. Today we have self-contained breathing apparatus, so please, firefighters, use it, even during overhaul operations.

The meeting with the assistant states attorney went well, but she was very thorough about the facts. The fire occurred in December of last year in a factory where the arsonist forgot to shut down the sprinkler system. I thought that there was a possibility that because there was this lay-off of twenty-two employees that they might have been involved. But the fact was that police Bomb and Arson detectives questioned some of the employees and found out the owner of the company had lost two major accounts that he had for pillows and blankets.

Special Agent Larry Adair from ATF was called in on the case. Adair was very thorough in his criminal investigation, and completed a background check on the owner. It seems that just before the fire, the owner bought an insurance policy for business interruption. Then he found out he was losing the big account with Wal-Mart for the pillows and blankets.

I was subpoenaed in the criminal case against the owner. I was commanded to appear in the United States District Court for the northern district of Illinois, located at the Dirksen Federal Building, at 219 South Dearborn Street, Courtroom 2117, on October 4, 1989. Matt said, "It's no big deal, Marshal. All you have to do is tell the court about your investigation." Well it was a big deal to me, because I had never done anything like this before. But Matt was right. They asked me about what I found and about my report and I was out of there in about half an hour. Special Agent Larry Adair called me a couple of days later and said the guy was convicted of fraud and arson. It was just another new experience in fire investigation, for me.

The Chicago Bears were playing the Green Bay Packers and I was invited to watch the game at Engine 45's firehouse, and have dinner. Firefighters are the most incredible cooks. We had a baked ham and scalloped potatoes for the early afternoon dinner. We had been watching the football game, and it was now in the fourth quarter. Most of Chicago's firefighters are Bear fans, and when we are in the firehouse the game just seems to be that much better, sitting back with your feet up and just relaxing. The score was Chicago 23, Green Bay 21, and there were only six minutes left in the game.

The speaker by the front desk crackles, "Forty-five-Engine 45, Truck 15 you have a fire." The yells from the back, "No no, not now!" and "You son of a bitch, there are only a few minutes left-that always happens!" I started to laugh because I don't have to go, but I will get the doors for them. As I looked around, it gave me a good feeling to watch them get ready to prepare for what may be all hell or just another run that don't amount to shit.

These young men were cocky and fast as they donned their fire clothes. The sound of the loud diesel engines reminded me of a time past. They jumped into their hip boots still complaining about missing the game on TV, and then the heavy nomex fire coats. In a whisk, they were out the door going north on Cottage Grove.

I closed the big overhead doors and ran back to the kitchen to see if the score had changed, because if I didn't, they would yell at me when they returned. I also listened to the fire radio to see if they had a fire. There was silence for a while, but the next sound on the radio was Englewood Alarm calling for OFI to meet the Twenty-second Battalion at a fire scene at 12610 South Michigan. Now I won't be able to see the end of the football game either.

The city of Chicago is twenty-five miles in length and fifteen miles across and I sure hope when I get out to 12710 S. Michigan, that no one up north like Engine 102 would need OFI, because it would take a half an hour even with the lights and siren blaring.

As the winter of 1989 sets in on the fire department, we all must remember to dress warmly and be smart about old man winter. He could really kick your ass.

In the early evening hours on December 22, Engine Company 107 was given a still alarm of fire. The fire was located at 2950 West Warren Boulevard. Upon their arrival on the scene, smoke was emanating from a church. Battalion Six requested a still and box alarm. Engine Company 107 led out a two-and-a-half-inch line through the side door into a large open area of the church. There was a red glow of fire toward the west end. The firefighters advanced the hose line into the center aisle. Slowly they continued to crawl through the heavy smoke. All of a sudden there was a loud crack and the roof of the structure just collapsed into the basement. The sound was almost like an explosion, and the heat and smoke drove the firefighters back, scrambling for their lives. It was not known for a minute or so that they were missing a man. Firefighter Kelvin Anderson, who only had about thirteen months on the job, did not make it out of the burning inferno. Frantically, the firefighters tried to reenter the church to rescue Firefighter Anderson, but to no avail.

A 2-11 alarm was requested and the fight continued. Fire Commissioner Orozco arrived on the scene and ordered a 3-11 alarm.

What was an attempt to rescue the lost firefighter, now became a recovery mission. In the subzero temperatures with winds out of the west blowing at eighteen miles per hour, they fought the blaze throughout the night into the early morning.

For the second day in a row, the fire commissioner requested a wrecking crane to lift the heavy timbers of the collapsed church in an effort to recover the lost firefighter. Mr. Hugh Heneghan of Heneghan Wrecking Company set up the large crane on Warren Boulevard. He had performed this task many times before, as he began excavating carefully the west end of the fallen structure. Many times the Main Fire Alarm Office called the commissioner to strike out the 3-11 alarm, and each time they were told that the fire is under control, but they would not strike out the fire until they had recovered Firefighter Kelvin Anderson.

While it seemed like an eternity, they found the young firefighter's body. He was ever so carefully lifted from the ruins of the collapsed building, on the day before Christmas Eve.

On a cold and cloudy morning, December 27, 1989, firefighters from Chicago, the suburbs, and across the nation assembled on Troy Avenue and Franklin Boulevard on Chicago's West Side. We awaited the pumper bearing the flag-draped casket of Firefighter Kelvin Anderson. Again the mournful sounds of the bagpipes could be heard as the pumper came to rest before the church. The casket of our fellow firefighter was ever so gently lifted and then came the loud voice, "Detail, hand salute!" and the white-gloved hands of hundreds of firefighters rose to salute their fallen comrade.

We closed the year of 1989 with the loss of one firefighter, but one was too many!

The investigation of the fire continued for the Office of Fire Investigation. After a cold, exhausted scene examination, Lieutenant Mike Deckelmann made the determination that the church's janitor had filled an aluminum pot with burning charcoal in an effort to defrost the frozen pipes in the kitchen area of the church basement. The fire traveled vertically upward through a pipe chase, and across the ceiling joists.

This was the area that the young firefighter fell through into the basement.

Chapter 9

On January 17, 1990, my son Tim enlisted in the United States Navy. He wanted to join the Navy and "see the world." I was not very happy with his decision, but I was proud of my son. My wife and I had never taken ourselves on a honeymoon because we could not afford one. Suzi had been promoted to a manager's position with CNA Insurance Company. As a firefighter I was making good money, so we decided to go to Hawaii in February.

The Office of Fire Investigation was starting to recruit the firefighters back that were let go in June. Arson fires in Chicago were at an all-time high, and we needed manpower. Each platoon got two more men, and I thought that Captain Moran would have been happy about the new manpower.

Matt called me into his cubicle one afternoon and told me he can't keep up with all the follow-up fires that have been assigned to him from Chief Burns. You could tell that the work had taken a toll on Matt. He was always tired looking. I told him that if he called me I would meet him at the scene.

Matt continued telling me that he missed all the camaraderie that was in a firehouse, the excitement of responding to fires and leading out hose up a gangway between two buildings.

"You might think I'm nuts Cos, but to me, momentarily not being able to breathe when the smoke banks down on you, and your holding that line, that's what I miss. The adrenaline that runs through a fireman when cinders, sparks, and smoke fall on you, and the air in the room is no longer fit to breathe, but you push forward and extinguish the fire. You beat it, and you win! There was no other feeling in the world like that.

"The job has changed for me," Matt said. "All I do all day is write reports and argue with Pat Burns because Chief Alletto is down on him to get the fire reports. Especially the big ones, like the art gallery. I never wanted to finish that fire report because I knew that fire was not a rekindle or an accident. I was told to shut up about the fire and get my report done. That fire broke my balls, Cos. I want you to learn everything there is to know about fire investigation, because you're young and strong."

"When I got into OFI, I wanted to do some good. Maybe catch an arsonist from hurting more people or solve an accidental fire, to prevent it from happening again. But that was a long time ago. You're good at this Cos. I have seen you in action, fire investigation is in your blood. I have books and more books about fire investigation, and when I retire they will be yours."

Matt looked up at the clock. It was a little after six, and he said, "Marshal you have kept me two extra hours and I can't put in for overtime." I helped him clean the snow off his black sedan and Matt left for home. I felt bad for Matt because he was such a great fireman. I also knew what he was talking about regarding not being included with the battle of putting out the fire.

In the very early morning hours of January 28, Engines 116 and 84, and Trucks 51 and 39 received a still alarm of fire at 6648 South Hermitage Avenue. Upon the arrival of Battalion Eighteen, Chief Foran, there was a heavy smoke and fire condition, and fire was noted issuing from the basement windows on the east side of the concerned structure. Immediately, Chief Foran requested a box alarm, and an EMS Emergency Plan 1. There were people trapped in the basement apartment. Engine 116 led out a two-and-a-half-inch line through the basement apartment, while the firefighters of Truck 51 made a forced entry into the structure. Members of Engine 84 noted that the flames that were issuing from the basement windows were blue in color. With three two-and-a-half-inch lines working the fire, it was extinguished in short order.

The firefighters were not quite ready for what they found in a small basement apartment. Natural gas was noted throughout the basement, and the bodies of a father, mother, and three babies were lying on the floor just inside the apartment door. The fire-fighters of the Eighteenth Battalion started to carry them to waiting ambulances as fast as they could. Paramedics from Ambulances 49, 18, and 14 started CPR and transported them to nearby hospitals. Chief Foran ordered the natural gas shut off in the building.

I found the cooking stove with all the burners and the oven in the "on" position. It became apparent that the cooking stove was being utilized to heat the basement apartment.

I then examined the cooking stove's gas pressure regulator. It's subjection to the continuous heat produced by the stove top burners caused the pressure regulator to begin to distend at a seam, which then caused it to malfunction and allowed the free flow of natural gas to escape. This fuel free burning caused high heat surrounding class A combustibles, and also caused the rapid spread of the fire throughout the basement apartment.

It appeared that the victims were asleep at the time of the fire. Once awakened, they became disoriented and were over-come by fumes, smoke, and heat. The loss of this whole family was very painful for the firefighters and will not be forgotten for some time.

February began just as bad as January left us. It has been a very tough winter on firefighters and equipment. By February 12, 1990, twenty-one people had died in Chicago in fires.

I was looking forward to my vacation to Hawaii. I booked the trip through my good friend and brother firefighter Rich Diver, who just happens to be a travel agent. I also was fortunate to have a neighbor named Kathy Barton who works at American Airlines. Kathy found out that this was our honeymoon and asked us if we would like to get bumped up to first class. Of course we said yes, and she told us that if first class was not filled maybe we could get seats.

Matt also knew that this was our honeymoon, and offered to drive us to the airport. The airplane ride was long, but once we arrived in Oahu it was fabulous. The overall temperature stays around seventy-five degrees throughout the year. The Pacific Ocean was as blue as I was told, from this island some 4,000 miles away from the mainland.

We stayed in a nice hotel on Waikiki Beach. Our room was facing the ocean on the fourteenth floor. In the middle of our first night, a loud bell rang suddenly. I jumped out of the bed and went to the door. I thought, what if there is a fire? I looked out in the hallway. There were a few people, but no smoke.

I put on my pants and told my wife Suzi that I would check this out, because I do know what happens in a high-rise fire. Finally the bell stopped ringing. I walked to the end of the hallway to check out the stairway down to the main lobby. There was no smoke, so I returned to my room and called the front desk. They informed me that there was a malfunction with the alarm, but no fire. I said okay, anyone can have a malfunction and I went back to bed.

Not long after I returned to the bed, the loud fire alarm began to ring again. Now my wife is very scared, and thinks that we both should get dressed and go to the lobby. I assured her that they are having trouble with their system. Again I put on my pants and shoes and went out into the hallway. The bell stopped, but now there were many people in the hall, so again I checked the stairway for smoke, no smoke. I returned to my room, looked over our balcony, no smoke, and again I assured my wife that everything is okay. I called the desk. We had a malfunction, but no fire. "Okay," I said.

Again I returned to my bed, but not ten minutes went by before the fire alarm went off again, and now I am really fucking pissed-off.

Instead of going out into the hallway, I called the front desk and he said, "Okay, don't worry sir, we had malfunction" in a Hawaiian accent.

"Put the manager on the phone," I demanded.

"This is Kak-mah, the hotel manager," he said.

I yelled over the phone, "Well Mr. Kak-mah, tomorrow morning I'm coming down and we-you and me-are going to do a little drill on the fire alarm system." I slammed the phone down.

My wife is now trying to calm me down. The clock says it is ten minutes to four in the morning. To me it feels like I don't know what time it is anymore. I got a beer and sat on the balcony and Suzi went back to bed. I went straight to the front desk that morning.

"Where is the manager?

I pulled him to the side and said, "I traveled some eight thousand miles to come out here to get away from fucking bells. I am a fireman, and I do get woken up in the middle of the night. That's my job," I said. "But when I am on vacation, please don't wake me three times with bells again."

Firefighters exstinguishing fire in the bank.

Suzi and I were treated to breakfast on the beach while the sun warmed me up on this February morning. Not too bad, I said to myself!

We went to see the memorial of the USS Arizona in Pearl Harbor. It was great. After telling a naval officer that my son Tim was in the Navy, we were treated as royals. The next day we flew to Maui and stayed at the Westin on Kaanapali Beach. My travel agent had a car for me and we went everywhere. The most overriding attraction at the Westin is the five pools all clustered together on several levels around an enormous sunning deck with a central island bar.

We returned to Chicago on March 3, and I still had six days left to my furlough. But, to my surprise Chief Alletto called me and said that Matt Moran had had chest pains the day before yesterday. He also told me that Mike Deckelmann and Wally Burke went to the ATF National Academy in Glencoe, Georgia for two weeks.

Alletto said, "I know you are still on furlough, Cos, but I

need help. Last night there was a 3-11 alarm fire at 222 South Riverside Plaza in the Loop." Mike Cucci, a marshal on the second shift had the fire, but he could not make a determination as to the cause of the fire at that time. With Matt down and Deckelmann out of town, he needed someone to start working on the follow-up investigation to document the cause of this fire.

Although I still hadn't even landed yet, I told Chief Alletto I would meet him at 1401 South Michigan in two hours. After reviewing Mike Cucci's incident report, Chief Alletto explained to me that there was a fire and then an explosion, and the windows on the east side of the first floor were blown out.

Somehow a rumor got to the vice president of the American National Bank, where the fire started. It was said that the cause could have been from a ballast in the ceiling light fixture. Alletto said, "This guy went nuts and called the mayor. Then the mayor called Fire Commissioner Orozco, and the commissioner called me." The vice president of the bank said, "Please don't tell me that this fire started in the ceiling, which is sixteen feet off the floor. You don't have explosions in banks in Chicago's Loop without an explanation."

Chief Alletto said, "I will make up the time to you," and thanked me as he walked out the backdoor of the firehouse.

Don Rimgale just looked at me and said, "Are you nuts? You came in off your furlough-for what?"

"Well, to help out Chief Alletto. Yeah, I guess I am nuts, but the challenge to do a big fire investigation, I think it will be worth my time."

First thing I had to do was to call Matt at home. We talked for a while. He told me that he had this pain in his chest in the region of the heart. "They called it angina pain, Marshal. No, no, not vagina, angina." We both started to laugh. "They want to do some more tests, so they got me on a lay-up. I told Matt about

Chief Alletto calling me back in from the furlough. He agreed with Marshal Rimgale that I was nuts.

Matt also told me to keep him informed about the bank fire, and if I need help to just call. I put my fire clothes in the red and black sedan marked 465, and grabbed a portable radio. Driving into the Loop was the first time I was able to think about where I was yesterday—Hawaii!

When I arrived at 222 South Riverside Plaza, it was about 1300. There were people running all over the place like nothing happened, but this is downtown Chicago. It never stops. Under this structure is the entrance to Union Station, and thousands of people come in and out these doors at 222 Riverside Plaza.

The structure is a thirty-five-story steel and concrete fire-resistant building. The exterior dimensions are 150 by 200 by 400 feet. I introduced myself to the security officer who was guarding the boarded up entrance door on the inside of the structure, along the east side. He informed me that he would have to call someone from the building management to let me inside the fire area. While I was waiting, I took a look around. The entrance area was all marble with plants and flowers leading up to the bank of elevators.

There were ten elevators leading up to the offices within this building. South of the elevators was a stairway and then all marble, just like the other side. But the east side of this lobby was boarded up just like the other end where I met the guard.

When I returned, the person from the management company was waiting. When I went to introduce myself, he started complaining about how the firemen did this and that to the building. Then he said, "and now you are here to investigate and waste more of the tax payers money." I pointed my finger at him and said, "Wait just a minute."

I tried to keep cool, but I couldn't. I told him that I was called in from my day off, and I don't want to be here, and as far as my brother firefighters, I am sure that they didn't want to be here either. So get the fuck out of my face, before I make a few calls.

This guy opened the padlock on the plywood door and then told me I couldn't go in until the tyvec suits were delivered because of the asbestos within the area. I pushed myself past him. He yelled, "You're going to get contaminated." I looked back at him and said, "I bet you didn't have tyvec suits for the firefighters last night. Get out of my face. I have work to do in here."

The fire was contained within a section along the east side of the structure on the first floor. The area involved was approximately 100 by 320 feet of floor space. This space was presently being occupied by the American National Bank of Chicago. The area was sectioned off as personal banking, institutional banking, and commercial banking. The section that had the greatest fire damage was the commercial banking section.

Within this area, there were nine desks spaced approximately three feet apart. The floor was carpeted with a rubber padding. Of the nine desks, five of them were totally consumed by fire, and the others were severely damaged. Each desk had a steel wastepaper container under it, and each container had burn patterns on the outside. There was an office type chair at each location and they were totally burned, including the seats and wheels. All that was left were the steel frames.

The carpeting in this area was burned away, other than a protected area under the desks or cabinets. I wondered why such a low burn, as it appears that this fire was out of proportion when comparing it to the fire load. There is something wrong: nine large wooden desks that are spaced about three to four feet apart. That is all that burned, just desks. I was very suspicious of the trash containers under each desk because somehow I thought

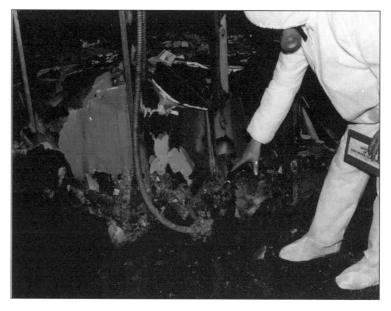

Author examining wires at the point of origin.

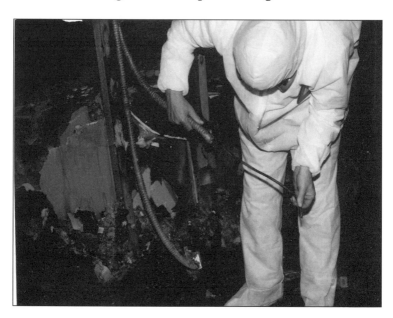

this fire might be arson. I left the building after locking up the door. I told the security guard that I would be back tomorrow, but this should be regarded as a crime scene.

I returned the next day with my good friends and special agents from ATF, John Maroca and Jack Malooly. Once again the manager of the building greeted me, and he told us that we must wear the protective clothing or we could not enter. I called Chief Alletto and he said to put the tyvec suits on for our own protection. Due to the high level of asbestos particulates in the air within the area of the fire, it would be in our interest to wear the tyvec suits, I thought to myself.

Temporary lighting was set up throughout the bank while we donned our tyvec suits and breathing apparatus. I just could not remember anyone worrying about firefighters well-being like this before. Then it dawned on me, this is the Loop, a bank, and big money. I wondered if they would go through all this fuss if this bank was at 4700 South Cottage Grove. As I turned the corner, someone dressed just like me in a white tyvec suit took my picture. I said, "Hey don't," and I realized it was John Maroca. He started laughing and said, "Cos, lighten up on the suit." I told him I looked like a pimp in this outfit.

With all my tools and cameras, we entered into this burned-out area of the bank. We began at the north end where the least amount of fire damage occurred, and worked our way to the south end of the bank, noting all the time the direction of fire travel by the lines of demarcation along the walls. We photographed everything as we made our way to the suspected point of origin in the southwest section. The windows on the east and west sides were blown out by the explosion. "This was one hell of a blast to blow out windows that were sixteen feet high," Maroca said. But why an explosion in a bank? That was the question that needed a plausible answer.

We examined the nine wooden desks, and the metal trash containers, which I thought had a suspicious nature to them. The manager told us that OSHA had a time limit that we could stay in this environment and we would then have to leave. We collected all of our samples for evidence and left the scene. I interviewed the night security guard that was on duty the night of the fire. He stated that one of the men who was cleaning the floors on the south entrance noticed smoke in the bank through the windows. After he told the guard, they both ran to look in through the bank windows.

They saw a small fire along the south wall on top of a cabinet. At this time, the guard and the cleaning person ran back to his desk and called 9-1-1. Then two guys who were working to refinish the elevator doors came running toward the desk saying there was a fire. They all went back to look again and there was a large explosion. The glass doors and windows came flying out toward them. Heat and smoke followed and they all retreated to the other side until the firefighters arrived on the scene.

The following morning, I set up a meeting with the employees of the bank. Those who attended were the bank's second vice president, the facilities manager, a security investigator, and a safety coordinator for the bank. The meeting took place at the American National Bank at 33 North LaSalle Street. This was the main bank. The one that had the fire was called the American National Gateway facility. In the discussion, we spoke about who locked up the bank and the last person to leave. They provided me with a copy of the alarm activity report. If any movement at all was made in the bank after 5 P.M., this alarm would sound.

When the signal went off, the time was 2222, which coordinates with the time the Fire Alarm Office's received the call. I learned who the employees were who smoked and where they sat. Also where the point of origin was located along the south wall. What I thought was a desk, was what they call a credenza with a printer on top. One of the secretaries who worked there was called in to tell me that the printer always had a pile of paper that would fall off the credenza or get stuck behind it. They were always moving the credenza to find some important papers. During the questioning, this young secretary stated that she would not go out of the glass doors when she left because there was always a wind blowing between the doors and it messed up her hair before she opened the door. At the time I didn't think much of that statement, but it was very important.

I reported what I had learned so far about the fire to Chief Alletto, which was not very much in four days. My regular shift would begin tomorrow and Pat Burns told me that we would have to suspend the investigation on the bank. There would only be two marshals working tomorrow and I would have to respond to fires.

There was a lot of report writing to finish on this follow-up investigation, so I did not say anything to Burns. But, I now knew too much about the bank fire and I was not going to suspend it until we had more manpower. On my way home, I stopped at my good friend Matt Moran's house to visit and see how he was doing. He said, "Marshal, I am ready to go back to work, but the doctors say I might need surgery on my heart."

He asked me about the bank fire, and how it was going. We talked about the fire for over two hours. Matt was so smart and he said somehow, someway I had to look for some type of flammable or combustible material, because banks don't have explosions. I sure do miss my good friend Matt. That is all I thought about driving home that night. I had about four progress reports that needed to be typed and Peggy helped me with all the reports and the photo index sheets that described each of the 200 photos

Flammables that were being used on elevator doors.

that I had taken of the bank.

This was my regular workday so I did some housecleaning, and made up my bunk because today I was going to get a little rest.

Pat Burns told me that some time today I would have to go down to the Fire Academy for film for the unit. The Chicago Photo Unit was called to the bank fire, so I would have a chance to talk to Bill Burnham and Tom McCarthy about the photos that were taken at the fire.

Tom McCarthy showed me the photos he had taken from both the interior and exterior of the structure. They were very helpful, because there were flammable/combustibles in the photos.

I returned to the bank and found out that the night of the fire a company was refinishing the elevator doors. Just outside the bank doors on the south end, these flammable/combustibles were lined up against the wall.

Late that night, I was returning from a fire on the North Side. I decided to drive by the bank and sure enough, they were still refinishing the elevator doors. The workers were using acetone, lacquer, and lacquer thinner, and the odor I smelled was just like the odor you would smell in an auto paint shop! Matt was right about the flammables, but the bank was locked up tight. How did they get into the bank to cause the explosion?

After interviewing the men who were using the flammables on the elevator doors, they stated they stripped the old lacquer off, then cleaned the surface with acetone, and sprayed new lacquer finish on the doors. The used rags were thrown in a five-gallon bucket in the hallway in front of the bank's glass doors. Across the lobby of the building were glass doors that were identical to the doors that were blown apart by the explosion.

The security guard who was working the night of the fire was in his station. I asked him about the glass doors and the lock system. He escorted me to the glass doors that were on the other side of the lobby. While he was explaining the lock he had a cigarette in his mouth. The smoke from the cigarette was being pulled into the store. As he talked, the smoke continued to be sucked in between the space in the center of the doors.

All of a sudden I knew! I thanked him for his help. I got my tool box from the red and black sedan and measured the space all around the doors. There was a one-fourth-inch gap all around the doors and a three-eighth-inch gap between the doors where they met in the center. The double glass doors were seven feet high.

I returned to the firehouse at 1401 South Michigan. The other person I was working with had a fire in the Fifth Battalion on the North Side. It was three in the morning. I was so excited. I wanted to call Matt, but I didn't.

I looked up the flash point of acetone, lacquer, and lacquer thinner in the fire protection handbook. All three of these chemicals are hydrocarbons and heavier than air, and have a flash point rate of 3, the highest rate is 4. Later that morning, I called Rich Kragh of Kragh Engineering of North Aurora. Rich had taken the remains of the printer that was on top of the credenza to examine the printer and the cord. Sure enough, there was an electrical failure in the cord leading to the printer.

I called Matt, and told him of my findings. He said, "Marshal, you done good, and if you want, I will help you write your report." I also told Chief Alletto and he said, "I knew you would find the cause, you're tenacious!" He said to take my time on the report and that he would give Commissioner Orozco a verbal report. Chief Alletto gave me an "attaboy" for a job well done, and his compliment made me feel like everything was worthwhile!

Matt and I completed my report on his kitchen table. The next day I met with Chief Alletto in his office at city hall and he approved the report.

The final report read something like this. After the eyewitness saw a fire on this credenza that was the result of an electrical malfunction of the cord on this printer, the fire escalated upward igniting paper and other class A combustibles. The low burn patterns noted across the floor, and the heavy volume of fire in the absence of a really significant fire load, in my opinion, can only be ascribed to flammable vapors being pulled into the bank from the area immediately outside of the bank doors where workmen were utilizing acetone, lacquer, and lacquer thinner to refurbish elevator doors in the subject area. These flammable vapors were brought into the bank via the glass double doors located at the south entrance of the bank. These subject doors, which are approximately seven feet in height had a one-fourth-inch clearance at each hinge area, and a three-eighth-inch opening where the doors meet to open and close.

My further investigation disclosed that the absence of a threshold and the absence of an astral between the doors allowed the air from the lobby where said workmen were using flammable materials, to enter the bank. This caused a build up of said vapors at low levels in the bank. The fire on the credenza ignited the flammable vapors on the floor, and this resulted in a major explosion.

Following the investigation of the bank fire, I was given letters from both Tishman Seyer Properties, managers of the thirty-five-story building, and American National Bank, on a job well done.

I think the best part of the investigation, however, was the attaboys from Chief Alletto, and the other investigators in OFI. It made me feel I had accomplished something of significant importance.

Chapter 10

ELECTIONS FOR PRESIDENT OF OUR UNION WERE APPROACHING, AND I received a call from Captain Tim Hynes of Engine Company 45. Captain Hynes told me that my good friend and fellow Truck 15 firefighter, Rich Wagner, was running for the president of Local 2. He wanted to know if I would support him in the election. Well, he really didn't have to ask me. Wags, in my opinion was, and still is, the best truckman on the job. I told Hynes anything I could do to help Wags get elected, he just needed to tell me.

One morning in early May, I got to work at about 0700. It was a warm day and things were going great in OFI. We had more manpower, which resulted in less paperwork and report writing. Pat Burns called me into his office and said, "Marshal, there was a fire in the State of Illinois Building last night." Pat said the fire was small and there was no response by the fire department. He also said that there was no hurry, but they still wanted an investigation, and some documentation. After checking out the red and black sedan, I responded to the State of Illinois Building.

I parked the sedan on Randolph Street in front of the building. I took my radio, fire helmet and notebook and proceeded into the building.

The fire was reported on the sixth floor in one of the office cubicles. I met with a Mrs. Mary Adams, and she showed me the burned-out fire in a wastebasket. There were burn patterns in the corner that indicated the fire ran out of fuel. The cause was most likely a discarded cigarette, or as we were taught by Chief Alletto to say, "misuse of smoking materials."

Upon returning to the first floor of the building, I was on my way out when I noticed that the red and black sedan was gone! At first, I thought I parked it on Clark Street, but no, it was gone! A police officer was directing traffic on the corner. I signaled him to the curb. Here I am standing on the corner of Randolph and Clark in a fire helmet. I looked like a fucking idiot. I told the cop that someone stole the fire car.

He asked, "Where was it parked?" I pointed to the spot some twenty feet away. He started to laugh. "You got towed," he said.

"Towed!" I exclaimed. "What do you mean? Who the fuck would tow a fire car with lights?"

He said, "You can't park there." I told him I was on a fire investigation in the State of Illinois Building. "I can't help it buddy, there is no parking in the Loop."

Steam was coming off my head because I was so fucking mad. But now I have to go into city hall to tell Chief Alletto that some fucking nitwit has taken the fire car with all my fire gear. There was a firefighter at the front desk in room 105, the administrative office of the fire department. I told him I have to see Chief Alletto, and this guy asked me if I had an appointment.

I looked at him and said, "Listen, you stupid son of a bitch, call Alletto right now or I am just going through those doors."

The door opened and there stood Terri Nardi, the fire commissioner's secretary. "What's all the noise about Billy?"

"I have to see Chief Alletto right now."

She said, "Calm down, what's wrong?"

I didn't want to tell her, but I had to. "Someone towed my fire car," I said in a loud voice. She started to laugh and I stopped her. I said, "Get him right now."

"Okay, okay, Billy, take it easy."

The next thing I know, I saw Alletto. "What's wrong Bill?"

I told him. It doesn't take much to get him going, and he started yelling, "Those stupid motherfuckers!"

Terri said, "Hold on, let me make some calls. I will take care of everything. Just calm down." Chief Alletto returned to his staff meeting. Not only is Terri Nardi pretty, but she is very important and had people running for cover in the Streets and Sanitation Department.

Terri found out that the car was towed to a yard on the West Side. They told her there would be a charge of one hundred fifty dollars for the tow. She told the guy on the phone that he would be paying for the tow with his ass and would be lucky to be sweeping curbs for the rest of his life. Now she was mad and had Eileen Carey on the phone. Eileen Carey is the commissioner of the Streets and Sanitation Department.

In a minute, the whole thing was straightened out, and they apologized. But I didn't have any way to get out to the yard to get the car. Soon, one of the drivers took me to get my car. Thanks to Terri Nardi, who takes care of things like this every day.

Late that afternoon, Pat Burns came into the kitchen and said, "Guess who's coming to visit our firehouse? Ron Howard, the movie director. He is going to make a movie about firefighters in Chicago."

We started straightening up the firehouse and cleaned the kitchen up a little before he arrived. Sure enough, a black fire department sedan pulled up in front of the firehouse. It was Stanley Span, who is the fire department ombudsman. Stan was a firefighter and worked on the West Side. He came down to city hall with Fire Commissioner Galante, and was in charge of all special events for the fire department.

Shortly after, a dark gray van pulled up and the next thing I knew Ron Howard was getting out right in front, along with many other people who were working on this movie about fire-fighters. After being introduced to Mr. Howard, we gave them a ten-cent tour of the firehouse. They were very impressed with this old type of firehouse. Pat Burns brought them all into his office and enlightened them with many stories of the fire department. They all left our firehouse with Pat. I think they went to the Fire Academy. One of the movie people came back to take some photos of the house. Michael Malone, who was the location manager, told me he needed to see some interesting firehouses like this one at 1401 South Michigan.

My brother, Mike, had stopped by for some coffee, and I introduced him to Mike Malone. We talked about many fire-houses, but it was my opinion that one of the best old firehouses in the city was Engine 65's house at Archer Avenue and Sacramento.

Mike Malone asked if we would show him 65's firehouse. "Sure," I said. We all went in my red and black sedan. I told him that there was a chance we could go to a fire because I was up for the next run. Mike Malone said that was okay with him, he would love to go to a working fire.

After looking at this very unique firehouse of Engine 65, he agreed that he would have to look hard to find one like that. We cruised around in Engine 45 and Truck 15's still district. He was looking for a row of brownstone buildings, and I knew just what he was talking about. We drove over to Forty-second and Drexel Boulevard. There were four brownstones along the west side of the street. Two of them were abandoned because of a fire some time ago. Malone thanked my brother and me and he gave us his card. Across the top of the card was written, *Backdraft*.

As time went by, Don Rimgale told me that the writer of the movie, Greg Widen, had interviewed him and Pat Burns over a year ago about the movie. He never thought anything would develop from it and he basically forgot that it might happen.

In the spring of 1990, my good friend and brother truckman Rich Wagner was elected president of the Chicago Firefighters' Union, Local 2.

Rich was always somehow involved with unions even before he became a Chicago firefighter. I remember him talking to all of us in Engine 45's house about when he was with Continental Can Company. He was a shop steward. Most of the firefighters in our house knew that Wags would someday run for a union office. He soon became the union steward for the Seventeenth Battalion, and later was elected as the business agent of the Fifth District.

I already knew he was a great firefighter, and I was sure he would make a great president of our union. With the union contract in place, a battalion chief with twenty years on the job was making an annual salary of almost $58,000. Just think, when Commissioner Quinn resigned, he was making $46,500 per year!

The radio crackled and the next voice I heard was Lieutenant Dennis Sobieski. "Engine 44 to Main, we have a working fire. Battalion Six to Main, three-story brick occupied, 50 by 75 feet fire on the rear porch."

"Message received Battalion Six, you are now getting Squad 1 to your fire."

I looked up at the clock on the wall, it was 1428.

"Battalion Six to Main," I could hear the trembling in Chief Montgomery's voice. "Emergency, give us a box."

The Main Fire Alarm Office repeated, "A still and box alarm 2562 West Washington Street."

The marshal line rang. "Cosgrove, we need an OFI car at the still and box." It was Kenny Little in the Main Fire Alarm Office.

"Okay Ken," I said, "4-6-4 is responding to 2562 West Washington."

"That's right, Cos."

As I was racing through the city, I could hear Chief Montgomery ordering Engine 57 to the rear and then he called for an ambulance. Shit, I said to myself, a still and box with injuries. I will be writing all night again. As I parked the car on the corner, there was still a lot of fire in the rear of the building. Engine 44's hose line stretched from the alley into the rear of the burned structure.

I met Chief Montgomery in front of the structure, and he informed me that there was a heavy smoke and fire condition upon his arrival at the scene. Most of the fire was in the rear of the structure, and there was a kid in the ambulance.

I followed Engine 57's two-and-a-half-inch line in the front door. As I walked through the smoke-filled apartment, you could hear glass breaking and firefighters yelling for more hose line. In the kitchen of the first floor, there were burn patterns that indicated that the fire originated outside and burned into the kitchen. I met Dennis Sobieski of Engine 44. They had their line on the rear porch. "Good stop, boys," I said.

"We hit it with the deck gun first, Cos," Denny said.

"Thank God for the deck gun," I said.

"Hey Cos, there's a kid in the ambulance. The uncle said he was playing with matches."

"I will be back," I said. As I walked out the rear door and down the heavily charred stairs leading to the ground, I saw that Ambulance 44 was parked on the corner of Washington and Rockwell.

I opened the side door of the ambulance and introduced

myself to the paramedic, Anna Rosa. She told me the young man inside the ambulance had burns all over him. Tears were streaming down the young boy's face.

"Hey, little guy," I said, "How old are you?" He told me eight years old. I asked him if I could look at his burns, and that I wouldn't touch them. I handed him my radio and asked if he could hold this for me.

"Sure," he said. I examined the burns on his face. He had a good size round burn on his forehead just above his left eye. He also had small burns on his thumb and index finger of his right hand.

"What's your name?" I asked him.

"Maurice."

"How old are you, Maurice?"

"Seven," he said. I asked if he saw the fire. "Yes," he said, shaking his head.

"Where did you see the fire?"

"On the door."

"Oh, the door on the back porch." As I was looking at the burns on his feet, I asked him how the fire started on the back porch.

Immediately, he started crying again, and I told him, "No, no, it's okay and no one is mad at you." I assured the little boy that no one was mad at him. Again I asked him, "How did this fire start, Maurice?" and he shrugged his shoulders. "Did you use a lighter or matches," I asked.

Again the tears began to flow and before I asked anything else he said, "Matches."

"It is okay, Maurice." I couldn't believe he just told me. The paramedic looked at me like, hey, good going! I told Maurice that everything was okay and I backed out of the ambulance.

I asked Anna where she was going, what hospital.

"Children's Memorial on Fullerton," she said.

"Okay, then, I might see you there if I need anything else," and I said goodbye to Maurice. As I was walking back to the fire, I thought to myself, "Boy, your mamma's going to beat your ass!"

I informed Chief Montgomery about the boy and we asked the mother where she was when the fire started. "I was washing my car in the vacant lot next door," she answered, with a fucking, arrogant attitude. We all picked up and returned to our quarters. This one was an easy one to solve for me. I drove over to Lake Michigan and drove south on Lake Shore Drive. We had three cars working today, which was good because I would have some time. I stopped on Grand Avenue and bought two hot dogs and a large coke. I drove over to the filtration plant and sat on the grass and ate my hot dogs. It was very peaceful here and I liked watching the boats go by. I often used this location to start my reports and sort though my field notes, while I rested after the yelling and screaming at the fire scenes. It relaxed me, and prepared me for the next run.

As the warm summer month of July began, I visited the lake after each run, and I was able to work on my reports and still listen for fires. There was no air conditioning in the firehouse at 1401 South Michigan. The only air conditioning was an old unit in the kitchen and Pat Burns had one in his office that vented out onto the apparatus floor.

Chief Alletto stopped in to say hello after working at city hall all day. He said that Robert De Niro was going to stop at city hall and meet all the commissioners. Also, he wanted to talk about fire investigation because of his role in the movie as an investigator. Chief Alletto asked me if I wanted to meet him. "I sure would," I said. "What time do you want me there?" "Well, you get off at 0800, so about 0830, be at my office.

I walked into the firehouse, and Emmett McShane said,

"Hey, Cos, the third shift is working, what are you doing here?" I told him I was going to meet De Niro at Alletto's office this morning.

"Not you too! Rimgale and Burns, and now you are all fucking movie stars."

"No, no, I am just going to meet him, that's all," I said.

Emmett said, "Burns and Rimgale have scripts, and they already know their fucking parts!"

"I can assure you, Emmett, I am not involved. Alletto called me and asked if I wanted to meet him. I said yes-so will you give me a ride downtown?"

"Sure, Marshal."

Then Rimgale came around the corner. "Hey, what are you doing here?" I told him what I told Emmett.

Rim said, "Did you know De Niro is playing me as a fire investigator?"

"No, Don, I didn't even know he was in the movie until yesterday when Chief Alletto stopped by."

Don Rimgale said, "You don't know what the movie is about?" I said no. "Well, Kevin Casey is in the movie, and there are three other firefighters. They told both Pat and me that we will have speaking parts."

"I think that's great, Don, I am sure you will do good." (I said to myself, this man really thinks he's going to be a fucking movie star!)

Emmett and I jumped into 464 and he drove me downtown. I asked him why he wasn't in the movie. Emmett just looked at me with a stare and said, I could give a fuck about that movie. I just laughed, thanks for the ride. Room 105 at city hall was jumping. People were vacuuming the rugs, dusting everything off. I walked into Alletto's office. He was sitting behind his desk looking at incident reports like he always does.

Someone yelled, "Here he is!" Sure enough, Mr. Robert De Niro walked in and starts shaking hands. He didn't look very important. He had a heavy beard and his hair was uncombed. He had a pair of Dockers on and a T-shirt. I stood back and watched as he went from one person to the next shaking their hands and sometimes taking photos. Finally, Robert De Niro was introduced to Bill Alletto. He told De Niro that he was the one who established the Office of Fire Investigation in Chicago, at Commissioner Galante's request.

Bill turned and said, "Here is one of my best investigators, Bill Cosgrove." We shook hands and De Niro said, "This is what you do, investigate fires?"

"Yes," I answered, "that's what I do."

"Are you working today?"

"No, I am off duty."

Chief Alletto told De Niro that I had just solved a major fire in a bank a few months ago, and that I'd done an excellent job.

De Niro asked, "Was it arson?

"Well, when I first started the job it sure looked suspicious, but it ended up to be an accidental fire."

De Niro said he was going over to OFI to talk to Pat Burns. I said, "That's my firehouse."

"Maybe I'll see you there."

"Yeah, sure thing."

Tom Purdy, an investigator from OFI, called to ask if I wanted to take De Niro to any working fires. We not only took Robert De Niro, but also Ron Howard, the director. We were all very excited when the first fire came in. I drove with Bob in the front seat with Tom and Ron Howard in the back seat.

At the fire, Ron Howard was asking why this and why that . . . De Niro could not get a word in around Ron. When we were putting our gear away, Bob told us he needed to know more. Ron

The author and Robert DeNiro at the 3-11 alarm on the North Side of Chicago.

was the director and he really doesn't need to know and asked if there are more fires. We won't tell Red what Deniro said. Tom and I dropped them off and we sat by the lake for a while before returning. I went to bed because the next day I was on duty.

The next morning I was putting my gear in the rig when all of a sudden, Robert De Niro is standing next to me. I asked him what he was doing there so early and he said Pat Burns had called early that morning to ask if he wanted to see an arson murder. De Niro added, "This is why I came to Chicago. Hey Cos, I really had a good time at the fire last night."

Pat Burns was calling because they were leaving to take Bob to the fire. De Niro said, "Are you going to come along?"

"No," I said, "today I am on duty."

"Well, call me," Bob said, "if anything might be interesting."

Very early the next morning, the Fire Alarm Office called for an OFI car to respond to a 2-11 alarm on the North Side. I called and picked up De Niro at the Ritz Carlton Hotel, as it was on my way. After the fire, Bob had asked me about maybe stopping for some coffee. He didn't want to be seen in public. It was pouring rain outside, and it had been most of the night. The best coffee around was at White Castle, and we sat in a warm car talking about fires and the fire department. At one point in the conversation, Bob asked me why I hadn't asked him for an autograph.

I said, "I don't know why-maybe because you didn't ask me for mine." He looked at me with that De Niro look and we both started to laugh. We talked about our friend Bob Rice, a Chicago policeman who worked with De Niro on the movie *Midnight Run*. Rice was a neighbor of mine in Talley's Corner. It became very easy to talk to Robert De Niro, and from that time on, we were completely at ease with one another.

As I drove him back to the Ritz Carlton Hotel, he said, "Cos, I think you're a very good investigator. I think you could help me research my part in this movie. I will need a technical advisor. You know the city, the fire department, and to top it off, you know Bobby Rice. I would like to hire you as my technical advisor."

"Well, I am very flattered that you asked me," I said, "but the fire department is very political, as you know. I would have to get permission from Pat Burns and Deputy Fire Commissioner Bill Alletto, who would then need the final approval of Commissioner Orozco."

De Niro said, "Don't worry. I'll take care of everything."

I pulled the black and red sedan into the entrance to the Ritz Carlton Hotel. Bob extended his hand and said, "Thank you for everything, Cos. I mean it, I have learned a lot already." As De Niro got out of the car he added, "Oh, by the way, thanks for the warm socks. I will have them washed." We just laughed as he closed the door.

On my way back to 1401 South Michigan, I thought I gave the guy my socks and now my feet are cold. Well that's not the only cold I had that day, because for some reason everyone was very cold. Pat Burns was especially upset because I think he wanted to be Robert De Niro's technical advisor.

Chief Alletto called me at OFI. He said, "I just heard you were picked by De Niro. Well, the fire commissioner said you can take your furloughs or a withdrawal from the job." Chief Alletto and Commissioner Orozco both suggested that I take the furloughs, just in case I got hurt during the movie.

There are more details about this in my book, *Robert DeNiro and the Fireman.*

DeNiro called me at my house, and asked me if everything was all right. Yeah, sure, I told him, but I needed some sleep first.

I was told to go to the production office to pick up the car and fire gear for Mr. De Niro. I arrived at the Ritz Carlton and after learning the procedure on how to get to Bob's apartment on the twenty-fourth floor, he answered the door.

We sat in a dining room at a beautiful table. We had a beer and talked about the two working fires we had responded to yesterday. He told me he had learned a lot by observing what I did, but also what the fire department did at a fire scene. He told me that Pat Burns and Don Rimgale were good guys, but what they told him about the job he could look up in a history book.

Robert De Niro is a very much to the point guy. He said, "I

am here in Chicago for about forty-five days and then I am gone. Have you read the script, Cos?" I said no. "Well here is a copy, so you know what's happening while we're working. To begin with, we have only three fires to worry about in the movie. All three take place in an electrical outlet. So if we can concentrate on duplex outlets and a chemical called trychtichlorate, we should do just fine."

As the days and nights went by, we were responding to fires throughout the city and spent many nights by the lake. It was great to be involved in this movie, except for one thing: Bob told me that the technical advisor cannot be in the movie. At first I was a little upset, but like Bob told me, if you're in the movie, then you're done with the movie after your part. Robert De Niro and I became good friends during the shooting of *Backdraft*. There were parties because we both had birthdays during the movie, but most of the time we were working, and very hard, I might add. This man was a perfectionist!

During the summer of 1990, the film company, Imagine Entertainment, began setting fires across Chicago in old warehouses and abandoned buildings. Most of the scenes that were shot were the ones that Mr. De Niro was in because he had a movie starting in late August called Cape Fear, and we had to maintain a tight schedule.

The time passed so fast that forty-five days was almost a blur in a way. I took down some notes about the things we were doing. Not because I liked writing, but because when a set was being changed it could take two hours. Mr. De Niro would work in his trailer and I would sit outside or in the red and black sedan.

I was saddened in a way when Bob left to return to New York, but I also was happy because I was never home and had not spent any time with my wife or kids. I went right back to OFI, investigating fires. The movie continued as they began shooting scenes all over the city. I thought this movie was great for Chicago, but mostly, because at last the film industry had discovered the firefighter.

The firefighters that Ron Howard used in the movie were real Chicago firefighters: Cedric Young of Truck Company 11, Kevin Casey of Engine Company 117, and Richard Lexsee of Engine Company 82. Howard said, "The Chicago Fire Department is very aggressive and is a legendary department."

Ninety five percent of what you see in this film is real!

One day, Matt came down to visit the movie at Engine 49's old firehouse. I was able to introduce him to many people. His wife, Jan, had a great time and they stayed to watch a scene as it was being shot on camera.

Late one morning about 1100, a still alarm was given to Engine 23 and 109, Truck 32, and the Fourth Battalion. "Engine 23 to Main, Emergency give us a box." The fire was just north of Twenty-second Street on Fairfield. The rear of the structure was fully involved in fire. Engine Company 109 pulled up on a garage concrete slab on the corner and utilized their deck gun on the fast spreading fire on the rear wooden porch.

The aerial ladder of Truck 5 was being raised from the bed of the truck, carefully through the trees in front of the burning building. Engine 23 is ordered to drop two lines on the fire. One to protect the exposures of the wooden-framed building to the south, and the other one-and-three-fourth-inch hose line is over the shoulder of the pipeman entering through the front door of the subject structure.

There was a Hispanic woman screaming that her children were still up in the second-floor apartment.

Ambulance 33 had taken one man who was badly burned to Mount Sinai Hospital at Ogden and California. A 2-11 alarm was requested and also an EMS Plan 1. By the time I arrived, firefighters were just handing out the second-floor window the life-less body of a ten-year-old girl.

The big deck gun of Engine 109 was shut down and one-and-three-fourths-inch hand line advanced into the hot embers of what had been an enclosed rear wooden porch. One body had been found, but there still were two infants missing. I was able to talk with the hysterical mother, who was unable to stop crying. She stated that she was in the Laundromat on the corner and her live-in boyfriend was watching the kids until she could get back. She further stated that she had three girls, one ten years old and two twin girls, who were eighteen months old.

Fire Commissioner Orozco was now on the scene. He looked at me as I walked toward the fire building. He made a gesture toward me, "Do we have anything yet?" I looked down and shook my head no. The press was everywhere in the street in front of the building.

I reentered the fire building through the front door, and went up the front stairs to the second floor. The firefighters were washing down and performing salvage and overhaul procedures. There were clear indications that this fire originated on the second floor. Burn patterns indicated where the fire traveled from the kitchen area out toward what was a wooden enclosed porch. There was a kitchen table and some chairs located in the southwest corner of said kitchen. On the floor next to the table, I found a couple of small bottles of Crystal brand grain alcohol. On the label of the bottle it said, "Caution Flammable Liquid." Then at the table, I found a one-pint plastic bottle that was burned. But the label read "Warning Flammable." I looked around as the firefighters were working, pulling ceiling and side walls in pursuit of any fire in hidden places. I went into one of the bedrooms and on the dresser were more of these small grain alcohol glass bottles. I got a very bad feeling and returned to the mother to ask about the grain alcohol. She started calling him a motherfucker and goddamned drug addict! I asked who she ment. "My asshole boyfriend, that's who. He freebases cocaine with alcohol."

I remembered that in order to freebase cocaine, either or some, other paraphernalia such as grain alcohol is utilized. We had learned about freebasing in a class given by ATF Agents.

I asked the woman how he would freebase, and she told me he used aluminum foil and made a bowl that he poured grain alcohol into, and then lit the bowl on fire. I told the fire commissioner about the possibility of a drug-related fire. My brother, Mike, was now in the Media Affairs Office and he was at this fire scene. The commissioner told Mike not to make any statement until we knew for sure. The two children were still missing and for the most part, the fire was out. We were working in the rear porch area when I saw something on the stairway that had been burned. Two other firefighters were with me. Carefully we crawled up the already weakened stairway. They held back and I moved up one stair at a time, until I found the remains of the two girls.

Carefully, I handed them to the firefighters below me and they were taken to an awaiting police wagon in the alley, behind the structure. I left the scene and drove to Mount Sinai Hospital, which was only five minutes away.

Once at the hospital, I asked to see the man who was burned in the fire. There were doctors and nurses working on him in the emergency room. I asked his nurse if I could talk to him, and told her I am an investigator. She said, "It's out of the question, we are preparing him to be transported by helicopter to Loyola Hospital's Burn Center." I explained to her that if I could see his burns, I might be able to figure out how this fire occurred.

Again the nurse said no. I took her hand and looked her in the eyes and told her there were three dead children and I think that this nitwit was freebasing cocaine and started the fire. She knew that I was telling the truth. I said I just want to see his hands. The nurse started undoing the bandages on his hands. The skin just sagged off. That's all I wanted to see. The nurse said he had burns on his feet and face just like those on his hands. I told her I would be back. I ran to my fire car and raced back down California toward the fire scene.

The helicopter was landing in Douglas Park to transport this fucking drug addict to the Burn Center. Once I was back on the scene, I informed my brother, Mike, and the fire commissioner that this fire was, in fact, the result of this unknown man, who was freebasing cocaine and ignited the Class A combustibles in the kitchen and the rear wooden porch.

I stopped back at Mount Sinai Hospital to get the name and other identification of the idiot who started the fire. The nurse gave me a hug and said, you did your job. She knew how bad I felt about the children that died in the fire, and she also told me that the man died in transport to the Loyola Burn Center.

The movie *Backdraft* continued shooting at different locations throughout Chicago. Often I was called by Bill Baldwin and invited to the set to watch a special scene. I enjoyed watching them shoot the various scenes like when Billy Baldwin falls into the air shaft that is filled with water, but Kurt Russell jumps across the air shaft and turns off the flaming gas valve.

I think one of the most remarkable parts in this movie was Sunday, October 7, on Michigan Avenue. I think there were about 1,000 firefighters in full Class A uniforms in the "funeral procession."

On October 5th, I received a call from Robin Chambers in New York, and was informed that Bob would be in Chicago tomorrow afternoon. He was going to call me about the funeral procession on October 7.

I met Mr. De Niro in the bar on the twelfth floor of the Ritz Carlton. We had a few drinks and talked about the fire department. I told him about the drug addict and the three little girls who lost their lives in the fire. We also talked about the movie and how amazing the scenes were turning out. Bob told me about his new movie Cape Fear, but he was worried about his hair, because in this movie his hair had to be long. We said goodnight, because 0400 came real fast.

I found Bob's trailer parked on Wabash under the El tracks. It was great to see Ilona again, as she greeted me at the door. Bob was standing inside with his fire uniform on. "Hey Cos, I need some help with this sling on my arm," he said. "Sure," I said, "I will help you."

De Niro could not believe how many firefighters showed up for the movie's funeral procession. It was pouring rain and we made the walk from the Wrigley Building to Jackson three times. Everyone was soaking wet to the bone. Afterwards, we had a few drinks in the trailer. I told him I was very involved with the election of a good friend, Mike Sheehan, who was running for sheriff of Cook County. There was going to be a fundraiser at Tom and Pat Murphy's house in Hinsdale, where we shot the scene where he saved Billy and J. T. Walsh from that explosion.

"Hey, do you think I should go?" Bob asked.

"Sure, I will drive," I said. "We will have a good time and I know that if I take you, we will get home because we have to shoot tomorrow at 0500."

"Okay," Bob said. "I will call you later." Bob did call later, but he said he was too tired and we had to get up very early tomorrow for the cemetery scene. Bob asked me if I could take him to the airport after we finished at Graceland Cemetery. The cemetery was a very long day and it had rained most of the day. We packed all of Bob's personal belongings in my 1996 blue van, and again headed for Midway Airport.

This time I was invited onto the white jet airplane because the weather had grounded them for a while. We sat in the brown leather seats and talked about the good times we had.

DeNiro took off in his beautiful white jet and left Chicago. Shortly after he left, the movie was completed and Ron Howard, Billy Baldwin, and the rest of the movie people left Chicago. We ended the year of 1990 on a good note, because now there would be a movie about firefighters—Chicago firefighters.

Chapter 11

JANUARY CAME IN JUST LIKE THE REST OF THEM, COLD AND SNOWY. Back in August 1990 the Iraqi Army crossed into Kuwait. This bold move by Saddam Hussein had caused the United States to send ships filled with American soldiers. On one of those ships, the USS New Orleans, was my son Timothy.

The USS New Orleans left San Diego, California, just before Christmas with 2,000 United States Marines and 800 United States Navy sailors on board. They were going to meet many ships, including the aircraft carriers USS Independence and the USS Eisenhower. In all, about fifty warships were sent steaming toward the Persian Gulf. I did not like this. The news was coming in every day that the waiting game was over. Four hundred thirty thousand United States troops were now prepared to launch into battle against Iraq unless they withdrew from Kuwait by the January 15, 1991, an ultimatum given by President Bush.

Less than twenty-four hours after the expiration of the United States' deadline for Iraq's withdrawal, USA F-15 fighter bombers began taking off from bases in Saudi Arabia.

My son was part of a war, and he was all the way over on the other side of the world, and that scared the shit out of me! The

USS New Orleans (LPH-11) was a landing platform for attack helicopters. It carried an amphibious assault force of the US Marines. It seemed almost too easy to the military, it said in the newspaper. In the first days, the Navy launched 150 Tomahawk missiles, and more than 85 percent hit their targets. It gave me a little better feeling, knowing that America was kicking this Saddam guy's ass, with all these high tech weapons that were hitting their targets. But, I still did not sleep very well knowing that my son was over there.

January 21 was a Monday, and it was also Dr. Martin Luther King's birthday. This was a holiday and the first shift was working. It was a double-time day for the firefighters who worked today. I cleaned the snow from my van, my wife climbed in, and we set out for Chicago's Loop. I was going to drop Suzi off at CNA at Wabash and Jackson and continue to OFI at 1401 South Michigan. I entered Interstate 55 at Pulaski and merged to the left lane. Although traffic was light, it was a little slow until we passed Kedzie Avenue. As we picked up speed to about fifty-five miles per hour, there appeared an eighteen-wheeler semi two lanes over to my right. At first, it seemed the truck was merging to the left because in order to get off the expressway at Martin Luther King Drive, you would have to be in the two left lanes.

In a split second the semi crashed into the right front door on Suzi's side of the van. Now, speeding together with the tires screeching, we slammed into the concrete wall at Halsted Street. I was thrown through the windshield of my van, and I landed under or next to the very truck that had just crashed into me. Diesel fuel was pouring out of a split in the truck's fuel tank, and I was covered in this volatile material. My first instinct was to kick this truck driver's ass. But, as soon as I moved a little, I knew I was hurt and hurt bad. At this time, two men from another car had me pulled out from under the cab of the truck.

They carried me over about ten feet to a steel guardrail along the center of the interstate. One of the men gave me a rag and told me to hold it over my ear, because it was only attached by a small portion of skin on the bottom. As my arms held me up on the steel guardrail, blood and a lot of it was pouring out of the side of my head onto the white snow on the side of the interstate.

Help, help us please, God. I called for my wife Suzi. It seemed the fire department was on the scene in just a minute. I was placed on a backboard and pulled ever so carefully under the trailer of the truck that just hit me. I never imagined myself to be on a stretcher with firefighters and paramedics walking around me with their black fire coats with the yellow reflecting stripes. All I can think is this can't happen to me, it happens to other people, not me!

They lifted me up into Ambulance 19, and the paramedic, Mike Burns, was trying to stop the bleeding from my ear. The cervical collar that was put on me was now causing the ear to bleed because when they moved me, the collar pushed upward and blood was everywhere in the ambulance.

The pain in my back was so severe, but this paramedic was all by himself because his partner was with my wife. He took off the c-collar and bandaged my ear, then he rolled a blanket around my head and secured my head to the backboard with tape.

"Okay, Cos, we're going to Mercy Hospital right now!" I was growing very weak and scared because now I thought I was dying. I got very cold in the ambulance and started to lose consciousness.

As I was wheeled into the emergency room, the first person I met told me her husband was a firefighter. She said, "We are going to take good care of you!" Her name was Mary Chikerotis, the ER nurse. Tom McCarthy was in the ER, along with Father

Thomas Mulcrone, the fire department Chaplain, who tried to reassure me that everything would be all right. I asked Father Tom to find out about Suzi. Doctors and nurses were around me taking my vitals.

Father Tom returned and informed me that my Suzi was taken to Michael Reese Hospital and was doing very well. Mary, the nurse, said "Bill, you stink from this fuel, and we have to get these clothes off you."

They started cutting my new Chicago Bears sweater that I got for Christmas. I said, "No, don't cut it off," and the nurse said, "I have to, and we will get you another one."

A doctor told me that soon I would be in surgery and they would be able to relieve some of my pain. I tried to tell them to call my children and let them know. After surgery, and three days in the intensive care unit, I was taken to the upper floors of the hospital. When I was awakened, there at the foot of my hospital bed was a three-foot by four-foot poster of the movie *Backdraft*, which had been sent by Ron Howard.

The room was filled with flowers and plants sent by so many people. I was still so weak. I kept dozing off into a deep sleep. My kids were with me and fed me ice chips whenever I was awake. My daughter Tracy told me that Suzi was doing much better and also that she was not injured as bad as I was. Dr. William Allen became my doctor and explained what injuries I had sustained. "Number one, you had an almost total loss of the right ear with a long laceration of approximately (20 cm) in length. The reason you were in intensive care is because there was a cardiac contusion to the heart. X-rays of your back showed fractures of the T-3 and T-4 vertebral bodies."

An MRI was ordered and a small fragment of the T-3 vertebral body was seen protruding into the spinal canal and spinal cord. The pain that I was experiencing on my right side was from fractures of the third, fifth, and sixth ribs. The doctor continued as my children held my hand, "We are going to put you in a Florida brace during the next three weeks with total bed rest."

Billy Baldwin called and sent flowers. I couldn't talk very long, but it was good to hear his voice. Bill Bracken, a firefighter, was downtown at the rally for firefighter's kids who were in the Persian Gulf. He brought my brother Pat in from Minnesota with all the firemen. They almost kicked me out of the hospital with them when the nurse found out how many guys came up. That night, Robert De Niro called from Florida, and he was so concerned. We talked about half an hour. I finally was able to speak with Suzi, after nine days. The first thing she said to me was "Where the hell are you ?!"

I was stunned on the phone. I told her about the accident. She said, "That's a very bad excuse, Bill." Then she told me that the dog was writing checks, and she thought two of them would bounce. I had no idea that she was in such bad shape. She had sustained a closed head trauma and lost her short-term memory.

Two days later, I was discharged from the hospital. When I first saw my wife, she had cuts on her face, and was black and blue. Her right ear was severed in two and both of her knees were cut from glass. But we were alive and back holding on to each other.

The days ahead were very hard, but we started getting stronger. Every day I had to have someone take me back to Mercy Hospital to see Dr. Markus to rebandage the ear. The most important part of the visit to Dr. Norman Markus was to see if an infection was in the wound. So far, so good. I was readmitted to Mercy Hospital again on February 27, 1991 for yet another surgery. This surgery was for a large graft from my right shoulder. I caught a staph infection and had to stay in the hospital for seven more days. The infection was gone, and the new graft took.

Finally back home, I began the slow healing process. I had this steel Florida brace for my back and I could not go anywhere without wearing the brace. There was still a lot of pain in the upper half of my back.

One day, I had a doctor's appointment with an orthopedic surgeon on 3500 South Michigan Avenue. I needed a ride, and I called my good friend Jim Kuknyo, who was one of the fire-fighters who jumped out the window on Fifty-third and Federal. He was still in bad shape, and had been on crutches for a year or more, but he was able to drive and took me to see this back doctor.

The waiting room was full of people and the two of us limped over to a seat along the wall. Kuknyo was a good fire-fighter on Engine 45, and he also was a very good practical joker. I had to stand up because sitting there so long hurt. I thought I would try to go to the bathroom. In the meantime, there were two women who were sitting across from us in the waiting room. While I was gone, the women asked what had happened to us, and Jim replied, "It was a skiing accident." He made up this story of how we were going down the mountain and went off a cliff.

As I returned from the bathroom, Kuknyo says he now has to go to the bathroom. Here I am sitting across from these two women with my head all bandaged and this brace. The one woman leaned forward and said, "It was a terrible accident-your friend told us."

"Yes," I said, "it was very bad."

She said, "Your friend said you loved skiing," and I nodded. Finally Kuknyo returns on his crutches, and he has this shitty smile on his face. I asked him what's up. He asked if I talked to these women, and broke out laughing. I said why? He told me then that he had told them we were both in a skiing accident. I said, "Jim, you're nuts!"

Well the two of us got into a fit of laughter, and these women thought we were both nuts. As much as it hurt to laugh, it was one of the best things that happened in a long time.

By the end of March, I was put into physical therapy and slowly I worked with this therapist, Paul Peptich. After about five weeks, Paul told me he did not think this therapy was working. He told me my entire thoracic spine was very warm to the touch and also very tender to the touch.

I returned to a spine surgeon, Dr. David Miz, and he ordered a MRI of my back. The MRI read that my back was not any better, and Dr. Miz recommended surgery. One afternoon, Jim Joyce stopped over at my house. I told him about what this doctor said. Jim was insistent that I talk to his doctor, Paul R. Meyer, a Professor of Orthopedic Surgery and the director of the Spinal Injury Center at Northwestern Memorial Hospital.

I collected all my X-rays and the MRI of my thoracic spine and set a date of May 5, 1991 to see Dr. Meyer. Dr. Meyer was over in the Persian Gulf as a part of a team of medical specialists and so he had a Dr. Haak evaluate my situation. The surgery would be a major procedure requiring a thoracic surgeon, a neurosurgeon, and an orthopedic surgeon. They anticipated I would wear a spinal orthosis for three to six months.

There were not too many choices for me now. This had to be fixed or I could end up in a wheelchair for the rest of my life. It was recommended that I start giving one unit of my blood per week before this surgery. The surgery was set for June 11, 1991, my son Brad's birthday. I had to prepare myself physically, mentally, and spiritually for what was yet to come.

The surgery took thirteen and a half hours, and in our language it went like this. They took out my fourth rib on the right side, removed my thoracic vertebrae number T—3, made a strut graft from my hip bone, and placed that where the vertebrae was, and I was fused from T-2 through T-6, with placement of steel rods on both sides of the spinal column.

I was fitted in a spinal orthosis for a long time. After the surgery, I was put into intensive care on a life support machine for about four days. My spinal injury was bad and I knew it. But, as the long nights and days went by, I knew I was getting stronger.

Finally, I was back in my home, which now looked like my hospital room. There was a hospital bed, a walker, and many special types of bathroom equipment. But I was home, and the love and support from my wife, kids and friends helped me get better. On my birthday, about two months after the surgery, I received a phone call from my good friend Robert De Niro. It was a great pick-me-up. We talked about an hour. He said he was coming back to Chicago to shoot a movie with Bill Murray called *Mad Dog and Glory*. We talked about my surgery and the recovery, and about what I was going to do. I told Bob as soon as I am better, I am going back on the fire department. There was silence on the phone. Then he said, "Okay, that's good, Cos, real good." He told me when he was starting the movie and said that he would call.

It was the first time I understood the reality that most people didn't think I was going back on the Chicago Fire Department. I called Bill Alletto and made a luncheon date with him. I told him I wanted to come back on the job, and he told me I would have to pass a physical before my one year was up, because after a year on lay-up, they put you on disability.

I was mad as hell. First I would have to get out of this stupid brace. Dr. Meyer told me one more month. I stopped at the movie set of *Mad Dog and Glory* and had lunch with De Niro. He was so nice to me, and said "Why don't you do some writing about your life experiences?" "I can't write," I answered. "I don't even know how to spell." We both laughed.

Firefighters who visited me said, "Cos, you were De Niro's driver, right?"

"No," I said, "I was his technical advisor."

"Yeah, right, that's what a buggy driver used to do for the chief."

I said, "What do you mean used to?"

Bob Gallapo said, "You mean you didn't hear they eliminated the chief's driver?"

How could they take the chief's driver away? The chief couldn't wipe his ass without the driver. Of course, efficiency experts will tell you that all the suburban department chiefs drive themselves. But in a big city like Chicago, the chief's driver performs many necessary functions to assist the battalion chief. I know firsthand, because I was a buggy driver in the busy Sixteenth Battalion, when Norm Doolan was off.

The chief's driver is, in my opinion, a position that needs to be filled and it is essential to the operation of the fire department. When an alarm is sounded, the chief officer has many concerns while responding to a fire scene. He should not have to worry about the route to be taken.

Upon the arrival on the scene, the chief should be able to access the incident and complete a size up of the situation without worrying about what the hell he is going to do about the black and red sedan, or where he will park it to get it out of the way of a truck or engine company. There is no doubt about this; the very first few minutes on a fire scene are crucial, and most major decisions are made in those minutes.

Battalion chiefs need to know more about fire investigation. Without his driver, he will have to depend on a fire marshal from the Office of Fire Investigation to make critical determinations about the cause of a fire.

Maybe it was a little selfish of me, but I always thought if I could not get back into OFI, I sure could be someone's driver. It was an important and necessary job that assholes around the mayor, who don't know the first thing about firefighting, but only know the fucking "bottom line," recommended.

Late one evening, I received a call from Matt Moran's wife, Jan. She was crying and had called to inform me that my good friend Matt had passed away. He was involved in a motor vehicle accident and died from complications that set in afterwards.

I was totally knocked off my feet with the news. He so loved to tell me about his new house in Florida, and the many firemen who had retired there. Matt gave me much encouragement while I was undergoing all my surgeries. He always said to me, "Try to get back into OFI, and attend all the schools you can on fire investigation. There is a great need for fire investigators down here in Florida. Maybe we could start our own business some day."

Matt would always tell me about firefighters he knew that died. He would say, "Marshal, he went up to the "Big Backstep" in the sky. I will miss him and all of his great humor. God bless him.

As time went by, I got rid of that brace, and returned to physical therapy. I knew it would be hard, but holy shit, I never thought I would have the trouble I experienced. First of all, I had three pretty therapists, and they had no sympathy for me!

Treatments consisted of cold packs, pulse ultrasound, high voltage stimulation, soft tissue massage of the thoracic spine, and (they say), pain-free stretching activities. Then, into the water for the aquatic fitness program that lasted for what seemed like endless hours!

Every day I drove out to Willowbrook at Plainfield Road and Route 83. After four gruesome months of this, the doctor brought me in for an evaluation. He is a specialist in rehabilitation, and one of the best. This doctor just went on about how great I was doing, and that he has never seen such a great recovery. He put all this sugar and spice in a speech, but in the end said, "You can't go back to the fire department! I know you're disappointed now, but you will understand later that it is the best decision, because it is a very dangerous job."

I tried to explain that I am an investigator and I don't perform the duties of a firefighter.

He just said, "No can do, Cosgrove, it is too risky."

I walked out of his office and talked to the girls who were my therapists. I told them what the doctor said. They kind of knew he would not let me go back. I informed them that this guy did not know who he was talking to, because I was going back on the job!

I know there are other things in life, and I am sure I could make it some way. But my father died as a result from this job, and so did my brother Jim. Neither one ever got to receive a pension. I am not going off on ordinary disability! I said to myself, somehow I will get back on the job. Jim Joyce broke his back and got back on the job. All I need is five more years to get my pension, the pension my father and brother didn't get.

I lay in my bed looking at the ceiling, trying to put things into perspective. Most people who told me I would never get back on that job have all but written me off. Even my friend Bill Alletto didn't think I would get back. But little did they know, that was what gave me the strength, because they thought no way. I was determined to get my job back!

I knew I would need a doctor and the only one who really knew me was Dr. Meyer. After all, he broke his back and he knew the limitations. I had to convince him that when I went back, I would return to the Office of Fire Investigation. The work was light, and most of it was paperwork. I called Dr. Meyer's office, and talked to his nurse, Nancy. She was the most wonderful person, and had taken care of me personally while I was in intensive care.

I told Nancy I needed to see Dr. Meyer right away. She thought something was wrong with my back. "No," I said, "I want the doctor to examine me before I see the Chicago Fire Department doctor." "Sure," she said, "we would have to see you. How about next week?"

I recognized the smell of the office, because Nancy always had cinnamon coffee brewing. A big hug and kiss from my favorite nurse. She told me I looked great, and put me in one of the examination rooms. Then through the door came Dr. Meyer. I think this guy could walk on water. When he puts his hand out to yours, you better be ready to get the handshake of your life, because he has a grip.

"How is your back, my friend," he says, as he shook my hand. "What can I do for you, and don't tell me you want to go back on that job!"

"Yes, my good doctor, that's why I am here. I want to go back for about five years, or until I am fifty years old in order to receive my pension." He told me he didn't think I was strong enough. "Yes, I am," I said. "I worked hard at therapy."

He looked into my eyes and said, "Okay, hit the floor and give me a fast twenty push-ups." I looked back at him. He knew I couldn't do push-ups. "Listen, I didn't want Joyce to return to the fire department, but he is a chief officer and physically, he would not have to perform strenuous physical duties. But," Dr. Meyer continued, "you are a firefighter and it's just too dangerous, Bill."

I explained to Dr. Meyer that as an investigator, my job would entail a lot of paperwork.

"I don't like it, I think you and Joyce are nuts. But if you can return to the Office of Fire Investigation and Dr. Russell thinks it's okay, then we will see you back here in one month.

I went to the fire department doctor and he said, "You must pass a physical. I have to tell you, Firefighter Cosgrove, this physical exam is very hard. I don't think you can make it."

I called Chief Alletto to tell him about what the doctors said. He told me that if I made it back, I would have to work days. Chief Alletto said that Don Rimgale had reconstructive surgery on his knee and he had to go through this physical examination that was conducted by a private company. Follow-up investigative activity, although very important, is much less hazardous, and you work days.

I called Don Rimgale to ask him about this key functional capacity assessment. Don said, "Cos, I won't bullshit you, this was hard, and it took about three-and-a-half hours to complete. He also gave me a copy of his exam so I could practice. Mike Gallapo also obtained a copy from a firefighter on the North Side. He also said, "Cos, this guy told me the exam is a bitch."

My friend Phil Lamm, who is a firefighter on Engine 126, had helped me with the snow, cutting my lawn, and fixing my cars. I told him about this exam. "Let's get to work," he said. Every day I worked out with Phil and by myself on performing the tests that are required on this examination, which would be taken at the Baxter Center for Industrial Rehabilitation, located in Bridgeview. I was ready for this key functional assessment. I can't say it was easy, but because I was mentally, physically and spiritually prepared, I was able to get through it with no trouble. This company was totally independent from the city of Chicago, and I passed this test to go back to work. Talk about happy!

Dr. Meyer said, "Hit the floor and give me twenty." I told him move out of my way. He just laughed and said, "Get out of here before I change my mind."

I walked into Chief Alletto's office and said, "Reporting for duty, sir." He said, "In all honesty, I never thought you would be back, but I'm really happy for you, Cos."

Chapter 12

THE OFFICE OF FIRE INVESTIGATION WAS SO DIFFERENT NOW, BECAUSE we moved to the fire department shops, located at 3015 West Thirty-first Street, and occupied the middle area of the second floor where the headquarter offices of the Bureau of Support Services were located.

The twenty-four hour investigators were now run out of Engine 44's firehouse, located at 412 North Kedzie Avenue. Probably one of the biggest changes at the Office of Fire Investigation was that Captain Moran had passed away. Also, Peggy Campagna had taken a maternity leave and was blessed with a baby boy, and would not return to the Office of Fire Investigation.

Pat Burns was the commanding officer of OFI and he welcomed me back. Although I was now doing follow-up fire investigations, I was very happy to be back at work.

It didn't take long, about two hours, before Pat Burns gave me my first fire. It was a follow-up investigation of an undetermined fire at 2048 West Seventy-ninth Street. The fire marshal who first responded to the fire was Ron Robinson. I called Ronnie to get myself familiar with the particulars of the fire.

Marshal Robinson stated that upon the arrival of Engine Company 129 and Truck 50, fire was issuing from the roof of the structure. Also, Truck 50 found the rear door unlocked and open. The fire occurred at 0020, and that's about all he could tell me.

I was given an all black, unmarked car and of course, it was junk, but like Matt always said, it don't carry hose or ladders and the heater works. Mike Deckelmann asked me if I wanted some help with my first fire. No thanks, I told him, but I will call you if I need any.

There is a strange and eerie feeling about a cold fire scene. I don't know how to explain the feeling. You remember how it was when you arrived when the fire was burning, because you have been there so many times before. But now the roof has fallen in on what was a restaurant that kind of looks like a McDonalds hamburger place, and it is a collapsed one-story mess.

The structure is all locked and boarded up. I could just pull a board back and enter, but we have rules. To reenter the structure now, three days after the fire, I will need to get a consent form signed by the owner, or absent that, an administrative warrant.

In an interview with the manager, he stated there had been gang activity in and around this restaurant. The day before the fire, he had had trouble with members of a gang when he told them they had to leave. At the time, they were sniffing cocaine right off the glass of the pinball machine! A two-gallon gas can was found on the ground behind the structure. Also, the police informed me that a burglary had occurred, and this fire might have been set to cover up the burglary.

I informed Chief Burns of my findings, and he told me that since the police were handling the burglary, the fire may have been deliberately set.

I was not very happy about just suspending this fire, but our job is to make the determination of whether the fire is incendiary or accidental. If it is incendiary and, therefore, a potential crime, the Chicago police take over and we as firemen move on to the next fire. There have been many changes on this job while I was laid up and before. One of those changes was Dan Fabrizio was elected president of our union. Now firefighters are provided with the latest state of the art protective clothing. There have been changes in apparatus technology and new equipment, like the air chisels and additional boss tools that we use for extrication. All members are equipped with fitted face masks and there are cross lay hose beds with one-and-three-fourths-inch hose for quick water and so many more improvements.

As I looked around the fire department, I thought to myself, the Chicago Fire Department always had a great reputation as one of the most progressive fire departments in the country. Every firefighter had about forty hours of training in the First Responder program. Even the dispatcher in our Fire Dispatch Center has been through the EMT program. If your fire gear gets a little "salty" all you have to do is bring it into the Commissary and they will replace it.

Many of these changes were the direct result of the sacrifices that were made by our retired members. Yes, the old timers laid the groundwork for these new and improved changes. I sure hope that they are never forgotten, because they did not benefit much from the changes, they just made it better for us. I hope the young kids coming on the job appreciate this!

The Chicago Fire Department shops are where all the apparatus is repaired and spare equipment is stored. Since I became a firefighter and many years before, the shops were a place that no one wanted to go. It was a place that immediately caused the morale of your company to disappear. The outside of the shops were filled with junk fire trucks that hadn't been moved in years, and also other pieces of city equipment that was junk somehow found its way to the shops' yard. Inside the building was a large cavernous hall about three stories high, and again there was junk piled everywhere. There was no place for firefighters and paramedics to sit while they waited for their rigs. The whole place was a total mess.

Deputy Fire Commissioner William Alletto was in charge of the Bureau of Support Services and took the shops as a challenge. He moved his offices to the shops, so that he could be a hands-on manager. Many changes were made. Number one, he cleaned out all the junk inside and outside the shops. If the rig could be used for parts then it was stored, but if it could not, it would be gone. The inside of the shops were cleaned and offices were constructed for Support Services administration and the Office of Fire Investigation.

This is where I now worked out of, a part of the OFI day group. There was Lieutenant Mike Deckelmann, Jack Lumsden, Casey Jabczynski, Joe Gruska, and myself, who went on follow-up investigations. The Chicago Fire Department now had command vans that responded to all still alarms within their districts, and all battalion chiefs drove themselves to fires, because of an asinine change.

Most importantly to me, is that the manpower was brought back, and you could, on occasion, have two marshals in one car. The twenty-four hour marshals were quartered at Engine 44's firehouse. There was a small section in the lower level where they made offices and sleeping quarters. One thing was for sure, there were plenty of fires and a lot of fire investigations across the city.

As the undetermined fires came into the day group, they were handed out to each marshal to do a follow-up. It was like assignment by caseload. Pat Burns measured all marshals to be equally competent to investigate any type of fire. Assignments were made by rotation and each succeeding fire was given to the next investigator. It was a fair way to assign cases, because no one investigator was overloaded with special cases.

Each week a schedule came out with a weekly response for back up fire marshal. If all the twenty-four hour fire marshals were tied up at fire scenes, then the Fire Alarm Office would dispatch the primary back up fire marshal for the next fire from his home.

Even with all the work that Chief Alletto had with the Bureau of Support Services, he always kept a close eye on OFI. Every day he would go through every report that was turned in by a fire marshal. If necessary, he would call you into his office and critique the report. It wasn't a bawling out, or a reprimand. It was very constructive, and a great way to learn. Chief Alletto called it constructive criticism and showed you how you could do a better job. Also, how you could avoid making the same mistake over again.

To Chief Alletto, training was of the utmost of importance. If you wanted time off to attend classes or a seminar pertaining to fire investigation, it was granted if at all possible.

Pat Burns gave me a follow-up to investigate on Monday, January 4, 1993. There was one fatality at this undetermined fire. A female was transported to the Cook County Morgue. I called my good friend, Roy Dames, to see if the woman had been identified, and she had been. Roy congratulated me on my return to the fire department and told me to come over to view the body. He gave me all the information that I needed and told me that one of his investigators would be at the scene. I met the investigator, Mr. Patrick Angelo, and began my investigation as to the cause of this fire.

At 0258, on Sunday, January 3, Engines 30 and 14, Trucks 19 and 28 and the Third Battalion were given a still alarm to 1703 West Augusta. Upon their arrival on the scene, fire was issuing from the rear of the structure and had extended to the structure to the east. Both buildings were wood-frame, two-story residential homes. Battalion Three requested a box alarm, and the engines began leading out into the burning building. Truck 19 began opening the roof while Truck 28 and Squad 1 began ventilation.

It had been raining mixed with snow, and the temperature was thirty-five degrees. As the battle went on to extinguish the fire, two firefighters found the victim hanging upside down from a floor joist in the rear section of the structure.

The fire was brought under control, and fire marshal Mike Cucci began his investigation. Cucci could not find a source of ignition, and found out that the gas and electric were turned off prior to this fire incident. During my on-scene investigation, I found the area of origin in a bathroom in the southeast section of the second floor. Irregular burn patterns in the floor of the bathroom led me in a downward direction under the suspected area of origin. In this room, I found what was the remains of a steel chaise lounge that you would use in a yard. Also, carpet padding and remnants of blankets. After sifting through the fire debris I found many used and unused candles with holders. The glass from the windows had a thick film of carbon, which is consistent with that of a slow-burning fire.

In an interview with the fire victim's niece, it was learned that this woman had lived by herself since the passing of her husband a few years ago. She further stated that her aunt did not have any gas or electric and had used candles for heat and light since she was a child. How sad, I thought to myself.

After a thorough scene examination and the elimination of all other accidental causal factors, it was my considered opinion that this fire was accidental, as a result of the improper placement of candles which ignited the bedding that the victim had used to sleep on in the bathroom.

Now all I had to do was write the report of the fire, which still took me four hours.

There was a seminar being held for cause and origin investigators at the University of Illinois campus in Chicago. I filled out the form and paid sixty dollars for a three-day class. Being back made me feel good, and I was logging seminars in one by one to learn all I could about fire investigation. The more I educated myself, the more I learned about the fires that I once fought. It takes a long time to be a good firefighter, and it takes an even longer time to be a good investigator.

I think that firefighting is probably the most important asset I have for investigating fires. Actual experience in firefighting gives one the opportunity to see firsthand how fire behaves in all its complex eccentricities. A good investigator needs to be thorough, patient, inquisitive, and curious. The fire investigator has to combine the skills that are needed which include experience, interview techniques, report writing, and a little intuition in order to figure out how each fire originated. It certainly never hurt that I knew something about building construction and the principles of electricity.

During the course of these many fire seminars that I have attended, I now know more about the phenomenon known as flashover, and how it affects us as firefighters. Today, we are arriving quickly on the scene of a fire, probably because of modern day communications and, like always, our fast push-outs and better apparatus.

Research has shown that time to flashover from open flame can be as short as one-and-a-half minutes in residential fire tests with contemporary type furnishings. Today, with the protection of a self-contained breathing apparatus, firefighters are able to advance into a fire building and get to the seat of a fire a lot faster than before. How many times we crawled on our fucking knees struggling to get to the seat of the fire, many times puking our guts out!

But, once you're in there, you just might precede the phenomenon known as flashover, and if so, you could be in for a world of trouble.

In my opinion, flashover has a sudden onset and doesn't allow much time for action, let alone any time to deliberate. When a moderate fire situation suddenly turns into full room involvement in a matter of seconds, a firefighter can be seriously injured or possibly killed. I think the only reliable warning that flashover is about to occur is a sudden unaccountable increase in temperature. But that warning only gives you seconds to react, if that!

I do know firsthand how unpredictable fire can behave, and just how difficult it is to define what is actually taking place at the time. I have studied many facts that say flashover usually occurs at or near the ignition temperature of carbon monoxide. That temperature is at or near 1128 degrees. If you feel this type of heat, and you don't have a two-and-a-half-inch line with you, get out and get out fast! That's one of the bad things about masks and all the protection we now wear. You don't get to feel the heat on your ears and face.

Chapter 13

IN THE MONTH OF MARCH, THE TEMPERATURE STARTED TO CHANGE, and again we would have another winter behind us.

A still alarm was given to Engines 4 and 98, and Tower Ladder 10, to a fire located at 1432 North LaSalle. Upon their arrival on the scene, Captain Ray Hoff of Tower Ladder 10 reported a working fire. Upon the arrival of Engine 4 he saw visible fire in the roof in the rear of the structure. There was a heavy smoke and fire condition. Many people were hanging out of windows on all the upper floors. At 0410 Lieutenant Martin Wirtz requested an "Emergency, give us a box" office.

The fire was located in the southwest corridor. Lieutenant Joseph Klem and Firefighters Barbara, Mahon, Gilliford, and Staatz of Engine 98 led out a two-and-a-half-inch line all the way to the southwest corridor. On the exterior, firefighters were faced with trapped residents of the single room occupancy, (SRO) Paxton Hotel. On every floor and in every window victims were screaming for help. The smoke that blew out above their heads was hot with a lot of force behind it.

The firefighters in the early minutes of the fire found there were more occupants in need of immediate rescue than there

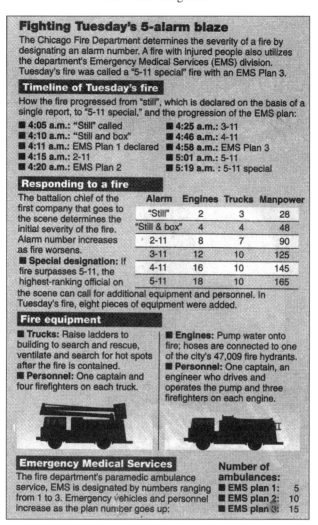

Fighting Tuesday's 5-alarm blaze

The Chicago Fire Department determines the severity of a fire by designating an alarm number. A fire with injured people also utilizes the department's Emergency Medical Services (EMS) division. Tuesday's fire was called a "5-11 special" fire with an EMS Plan 3.

Timeline of Tuesday's fire

How the fire progressed from "still", which is declared on the basis of a single report, to "5-11 special," and the progression of the EMS plan:

- **4:05 a.m.: "Still" called**
- **4:10 a.m.: "Still and box"**
- **4:11 a.m.: EMS Plan 1 declared**
- **4:15 a.m.: 2-11**
- **4:20 a.m.: EMS Plan 2**
- **4:25 a.m.: 3-11**
- **4:46 a.m.: 4-11**
- **4:58 a.m.: EMS Plan 3**
- **5:01 a.m.: 5-11**
- **5:19 a.m. : 5-11 special**

Responding to a fire

The battalion chief of the first company that goes to the scene determines the initial severity of the fire. Alarm number increases as fire worsens.
- **Special designation:** If fire surpasses 5-11, the highest-ranking official on the scene can call for additional equipment and personnel. In Tuesday's fire, eight pieces of equipment were added.

Alarm	Engines	Trucks	Manpower
"Still"	2	3	28
"Still & box"	4	4	48
2-11	8	7	90
3-11	12	10	125
4-11	16	10	145
5-11	18	10	165

Fire equipment

- **Trucks:** Raise ladders to building to search and rescue, ventilate and search for hot spots after the fire is contained.
- **Personnel:** One captain and four firefighters on each truck.

- **Engines:** Pump water onto fire; hoses are connected to one of the city's 47,009 fire hydrants.
- **Personnel:** One captain, an engineer who drives and operates the pump and three firefighters on each engine.

Emergency Medical Services

The fire department's paramedic ambulance service, EMS is designated by numbers ranging from 1 to 3. Emergency vehicles and personnel increase as the plan number goes up:

Number of ambulances:
- **EMS plan 1:** 5
- **EMS plan 2:** 10
- **EMS plan 3:** 15

An indicator of how fast the alarms came in at the Paxton Hotel fire.

were available ladders or firefighters. As more fire companies arrived, they found conditions to be critical and rapidly deteriorating.

Trapped residents became very desperate, and panic set in. Twenty, thirty, forty, and fifty-foot ladders are being thrown on all sides of the building, saving one life after the next. All you could hear was the screaming of victims and the screaming of sirens. As more help arrived, they started cutting steel bars from windows on the ground floor to free trapped victims.

Suddenly the fire blew a transformer in the alley, setting off a series of 12,000-volt explosions. The heavy smoke made it hard to see in the north alley, and firefighters only found people when a gust of wind would blow.

The horror spread as a woman lay in agony after leaping from the fourth floor. A man hung onto a downspout paralyzed by fear. A firefighter advanced up the thirty-foot ladder and rescued the man. Smoke and hot gases were billowing from all the windows. The area looked like a war zone crowded with the injured and dead lying all over the front of the structure. Some had jumped before the truck and engines got there. Finally the firefighters got some water from a point advantage, with hose lines right on the area of origin.

Firefighters with lifelines lowered a victim from a roof in the rear in a stokes basket. Two hundred seventy firefighters worked very hard until every person was rescued from the burning structure. Remarkably, over 100 people were rescued by these brave men and women of the Chicago Fire Department.

The darkness of night slowly changed to the light of day and master streams from tower ladders were now "surrounding and drowning" the Paxton Hotel. I arrived at the shops at 0630, and we were ordered by 2-1-8 Alletto to respond in the Office of Fire Investigation "Major Response Unit" to the fire. All investigators were requested to respond to the 5-11 alarm and report to Pat Burns. Jack Lumsden and I rode together in this MIRU unit, and arrived at the fire scene at 0710. People were still being taken to ambulances and were lined up and down the street. A team of paramedics were performing CPR on the wet street, waiting for

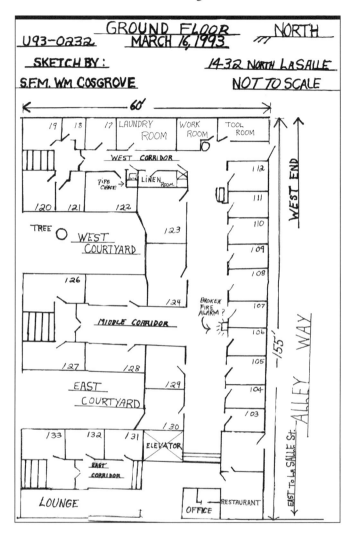

Ground floor of the Paxton Hotel. "Drawn" by the author the day of the fire.

the arrival of the next ambulance company.

The fire commissioner was now in charge of this fire. Ray Orozco looked the scene over as he began shutting down some of the master streams, in an effort to begin a last attempt rescue for anyone who might have survived this deadly blaze.

Pat Burns and I entered an office on the ground floor. The water was cascading through every opening in the ceiling above. We found a registry of the 140 guests. Resident rooms were occupied and several occupants had their own guest in his room for the night. In a little while, Fire Commissioner Orozco led a small team of chiefs, firefighters and marshals, into the burning building.

The very first victim was found in a sitting position in a closet just inside the door of room 133. We slowly started up a wooden stairway in the southeast section of the structure, heavy waterfalls beneath our feet and down the stairs. As we arrived on the second floor, a victim was found lying in the fetal position, in and under about eighteen inches of fire debris. Firefighters began breaching through the walls in an effort to reach the north end of the building. A third victim was found lying alongside the bathroom in room 237, and a fourth victim was found lying on his back in twenty-four inches of hot fire debris. The fifth victim was found in his room, 202, lying on his back in bed. He was burned beyond recognition.

We went back into the major incident response unit. We know there were many more victims and what had to be done. A sketch had to be made. Jack Lumsden handed me a small blueprint of the rooms in the hotel.

I was able to draw a better sketch and number the rooms, so we could begin to identify the dead. With cameras, notebooks, and flashlights, we were going back in to begin to mark the rooms and places that each body is found. The first victims were easy to photograph because we were there once before. We now went to the west end of the structure. Ladders were raised all along the alley and the rear of the building. I started to ascend the ladder and I hear a familiar voice. It was that of Father Tom Mulcrone. I bet Dr. Meyer would like this photo in his office,

Father said, and I looked to my left and next to me on a thirty-foot ladder is Deputy Fire Commissioner Jim Joyce. We made eye contact and shared a smile for there was a day when Joyce and I never thought we would ever be on a ladder again.

As we entered room 217, firefighters with their axes breaching through the walls are leading us through, so it is documented.

The victim in room 215 died trying to open the window. Room 217's victim also tried to open the window and escape the fire. The next victim was found upside down in the bathtub in room 219. Then I started being called all over the structure as firefighters continued to find victims. By 1400, we had some eleven victims recovered from the Paxton Hotel fire.

The search continued throughout the rest of the day for victims, and we all started to compile data from the places where the bodies were found. By 2200, we picked up and went home. At 0700, we were right back at 1432 North LaSalle, or should I say the day group was there. Pat Burns told us that they wanted to take the building down. We needed to obtain as much data and photographs as we could in a short time. "About how long?" I asked, and Pat said that in about two hours Hugh Heneghan was going to be coming around that corner and that's when we're done.

All day and all night, the police were saying they have a guy they like for starting the fire in room 121. Pat Burns said he wanted that room combed. Mike Deckelmann said he worked on room 121 and had an interview with a Mr. Yablong, who lived next door.

I went to the southwest corridors where the fire totally consumed all the fuel. All that was left was bricks, melted steel, and plaster piled two-and-a-half-feet high in the corridor. Emmett McShane walked up saying that we had to look at the electric panels in this corridor. We just looked up four stories and could

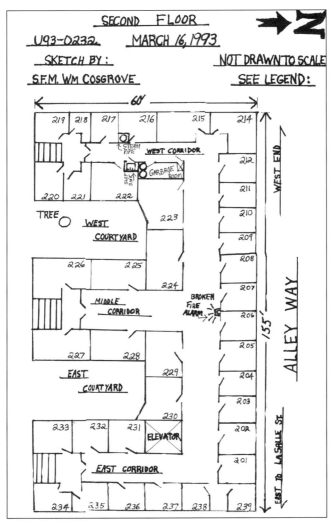

This is the second floor layout of the Paxton Hotel. "Drawn"

see the sky.

Emmett said, "This is where the fire originated, in this area."
We could see that all the fuel was gone. I climbed up to the third
floor. All you could see in this corridor was where fire brick walls
were sectioned by steel structural framing. From one floor to the

next and right out the roof were pipes from water lines and drain lines. I remembered what Matt said, "Stop for one minute and look through the long lens. Is this a set fire? Deep in your soul you say 'no,' but we don't know." Emmett said, "Cos let's get some photos of this."

He continued to shoot photo after photo of the southwest corridor. I began my cause and origin investigation to relate me with the structure.

The exterior examination of the structure disclosed it to be a four-story brick building with approximate exterior dimensions of 65 by 155 by 45. There were two courtyards located on the south side of the structure. The Paxton took the reverse E-shape look, if you will, from the LaSalle Street side.

Although the bearing walls were masonry and steel, the non-bearing walls separating rooms were constructed of two-by-four wood studs, and they were covered with plaster on lath. Wood joists were installed between the steel beams between the interior and exterior bearing walls. The joists were covered with hardwood flooring throughout.

Each floor had a long corridor that ran the depth of the building east and west. The long corridor connected to shorter corridors in the east, middle, and west sides of the building. The stairways that led up to the upper floors were of wood construction. Each corridor entrance also was originally equipped with fire doors. However, these doors were removed for the installation of new carpeting. This was a major factor in this fire's spread.

This building was equipped with a local in the structure alarm system. But, unfortunately, it was not working at the time of the fire. This also was a major factor in this fire.

Weather and lighting conditions at the time of the fire also played a significant role. The temperature was thirty-nine degrees, wind out of the south at twenty miles per hour and gusting to thirty miles per hour. The sky was overcast with light falling rain.

Upon entering the east side of the structure at ground level, the first room inside on the left appeared to be a lounge area with no fire damage. To our right was the office, and approximately twenty-five feet into the structure was an elevator which wasn't in working order, and had not been in use for a long time. Also on the ground floor was a Chinese restaurant-TSANG was the name. This corridor was to be further noted as "the long corridor." On the right side were rooms numbered 103 through 112, and on the left was room 129, and then the short corridor in the middle of the structure. The stairway in the middle corridor was impassible because of total collapse. Right there hanging on the wall was probably the largest fire bell I had ever seen that did not work. I proceeded to the west corridor, and on my right was a tool, work, and laundry room, and the remains of rooms 117, 118, and 119. On my left is the linen room that had a clothes chute that went up to all the linen rooms above to the fourth floor.

The next door south was the janitor's closet with a slop sink. There was a janitor's closet in the same place on all upper floors. The next three doors were rooms 122, 121, and 120. Rooms 120 and 121 were set back into an alcove with a wooden stairway leading upward to the upper floors. This west corridor was also impassible as a result of structural collapse. I climbed the three-foot pile of debris and photographed and sketched the rooms. There was no smoke or fire damage to the walls on the ground floor except by the slop sinks, where there was a complete burn-out of all combustible material.

Continuing the ground floor examination in the "long corridor" at the west end, was a small hallway leading to the tool room and the exterior service door leading out to the alley on the north side of the structure. There was no fire damage to any of the

Left side of photo depicts the garbage cans in front of the janitors closet. Note the slop sinks.

rooms in that short hallway. On the floor between rooms 111 and 112 was a dry chemical fire extinguisher that had not been used.

Affixed to the wall outside room 107 was this one and only large fire bell and it was not in working order. Something was very wrong because if this bell worked, it would have alerted the people across the street, along with the residents.

I ascended again up the front stairway in the southeast section of the structure. The stairs were wooden and there were seven steps that led to the landing between the first floor and the second floor. The next seven steps that led up to the second floor were filled with fire debris from the stairway that had collapsed from the upper floors.

Standing in the entranceway of the corridor on the second floor in the east section, I noted that there was total burn-out, from the second floor through the roof. All that was left were the twisted steel structural members. Five bodies were found in this corridor. I worked my way around the second floor through the breached walls that were made by the fire suppression companies.

I continued documenting damage and burn patterns, to use when we wouldn't have any structure to look at tomorrow. Hugh Heneghan was already moving toward the Paxton Hotel.

After a fast coffee, I moved to the rear of the concerned structure, looking at anything that would give me more information about the fire.

I had to climb a twenty-foot ladder to enter room 215 through the window. Cautiously, I approached the doorway in room 216. There was severe charring to this entrance and to my right was a pipe chase with an eight-inch steam pipe and many other water and drain lines within this pipe, that protruded upward to the roof area.

Directly outside of this doorway was the west corridor, which had collapsed to the ground floor, and all class A combustibles had been consumed. On the other side of the corridor, directly across from room 216, was the garbage room and what appeared to be three slop sinks which had fallen from the upper floors to the ground floor.

Also amongst the slop sinks were three fifty-five-gallon metal garbage cans lying in the debris. The can along the side of the slop sink had an eight-inch hole in the bottom of it, which appeared to be from rust and fire. There was no doubt in my mind that the worst fire damage to this structure was right here in front of the garbage room, and the janitor's closet where the slop sinks were located.

I continued my investigation throughout the second floor, photographing and also sketching and writing notes to myself.

In a room on the upper floor, firefighters found the human remains of a man's arm and leg. They were sketched, photographed, and bagged for the Cook County Morgue.

In room 121, Mike Deckelmann was conducting his investigation, which was where the police have said that Mr. Robinson has told them he spliced a set of wires on a portable electric space heater. The police have made Mr. Robinson's room their area of origin, where they believe the fire started from the splice job.

We entered room 121 off the west courtyard in between the center and the west sections of the building. A window was removed to give easy access to the room, and as I looked through this room I found Mike Deckelmann continuing his investigation. I moved toward the door of room 121 into an alcove that serviced rooms 120 and 121. This foyer had heavy fire damage to the top section. Both doors were heavily burned.

There was a fire door leaning against the wall that had been removed because of supposedly new carpeting. The west corridor was completely burned as all combustibles were consumed. But eight feet away in this alcove that leads into rooms 120 and 121, it is all intact-the walls are still painted plaster walls.

The word went out, Hugh Heneghan is now out in front setting up the crane to demolish the remains of the Paxton Hotel. Jack Lumsden and Emmett McShane were tape recording victims in OFI's unit in front of the building. They were going over the names of the people who lived in the Paxton hotel.

I met my brother Mike out in front of the building. I didn't have much chance before, but we now stated some of the facts about what we knew so far. Three victims died from jumping from the upper windows and Deputy District Chief Bill Nolan walked up and informed us of more. Ten victims were found in closets, hallways, and under beds throughout the structure.

Nolan continued, "Did you know this is the first 5-11 in nearly four years?" There were two hundred firefighters, forty paramedics and fifteen ambulances called to the fire.

Bill Nolan looked at me and said, "What about this space heater thing in room 121, what do you think?" I looked around and said this fire did not originate in that room. "Well, somebody better tell that to the police, Cos," Nolan said, "because they just made an announcement that the fire started from faulty wiring and is believed to be accidental. Chief Nolan signaled the fire commissioner and told him what I said.

Fire Commissioner Raymond Orozco said to the media that he was aware of the police findings, but was not making any official determination. I sure needed Chief Alletto now, I thought. He is conducting oral board examinations for new candidates for officer on the Chicago Fire Department.

Heneghan's giant red and black crane began to swing the large bucket with large steel jaws into the building. What we have as evidence is all we are going to get because the crane has begun to take the Paxton Hotel down, posthaste, due to structural instability.

Interview number one was with Mr. David Yablong of 1428 North LaSalle, one door to the south of the Paxton Hotel. Mr. Yablong informed me of how the fire burned, mainly in the rear west section. Fire was already issuing from the roof when he got outside. He also informed me that his father was the builder of the Paxton Hotel.

Interview number two was with Mr. James Parrillo in room 32 in Grant Hospital where he was being treated for smoke inhalation. Parrillo was eighty years old. He woke up to a smoke filled room. He said, "I grabbed a towel, my glasses, and my false teeth." He said he made his way down the hall toward the southeast stairway, when he tripped over a body. He turned around and went into a room toward a window where he was rescued down a ladder by a Chicago firefighter. Mr. Parrillo also informed me that in his thirty-five years at the Paxton Hotel, he had never seen a fire this bad. "We have had fires," he continued, "but most of the time we put them out ourselves." I asked Mr. Parrillo about how many fires they have had at the Paxton.

"About ten to twelve fires since I have lived here, only two bad ones, the rest were small fires in the garbage room."

That interview got me thinking-the worst fire damage was by the garbage room. I called engine 98's firehouse, located at 202 East Chicago Avenue. I spoke to Lieutenant Joe Klem and asked him if I could interview him and his crew. "Sure Cos," Joe said, "come for soup." I took him up on his offer and had a great bowl of vegetable soup.

We began looking up fires in the Paxton Hotel. Almost all the members of Engine 98 remembered being there on fire calls. They all agreed that there were a lot of fires in the garbage rooms. Of the seven or so fires in the Paxton Hotel, one was a still and box mattress fire, and the rest were from the garbage rooms that were on all floors. I was amazed at the lead out that Engine 98 made at the Paxton. Earlier I mentioned an engine company led out a two-and-a-half-inch line down the long corridor to the west corridor over a 200 foot lead out to the rear. The stairway was burning and fire was issuing from the ceiling area of the alcove. "Engine 98 began backing their line up; when I saw the ceiling above me falling down and fire behind, we backed out to the street," Klem said.

Lieutenant Klem also said when they were backing their line out the middle stairway had collapsed. Some ten minutes after the call, the wooden stairway collapsed. All I can think is maybe this is arson because this fire traveled way too fast.

There was another interview with a Mr. Hoper, who worked at a local pet store and lived in the Paxton Hotel. He could attest that there had been three fires. One was a small mattress fire, and they never called the fire department. He remembered one fire when he was taking his trash down to the garbage room and it was on fire. The fire department put that one out.

Mark Weglary, the resident manager of the Paxton Hotel, said that he heard about the fire from Mr. Robinson and Liza Huntley. They told him that there was a big fire. Get everyone out, he said, and he then called 9-1-1. Mr. Weglary then ran up to the third floor to tell his girlfriend to get out. He escaped the fire by scaling the six-inch ledge in the front of the building to a fifty-foot Bangor ladder.

Jack Lumsden and I drove up to the Wilson-Windsor Apartments on West Wilson Avenue, on the North Side. Wilson-Windsor is another single room occupancy hotel just like the Paxton Hotel. We found Mrs. Huntley and recorded her statement. She stated that she was in the third-floor southwest stairway at about ten minutes before 4 A.M. She is the hotel maid and begins her rounds very early. She said she had come down the long corridor to the west when all of a sudden she saw this crippled man in a wheelchair saying "Fire, fire!" Mrs. Huntley said she saw fire by Mr. Robinson's apartment, room 121. She had already given this statement to the police.

We returned to the scene to tell Pat Burns about the interviews. Heneghan continued pulling apart the structure that was once the Paxton Hotel. Pat informed us that some fourteen people are still missing, and were feared dead. Throughout the night, two more bodies were discovered, and taken from the ruins of this horror. The police are firm that this crippled man is responsible for the fire, but it sounds a little fishy. Let's get Alletto here. We went through all the evidence I had on the garbage and the total destruction of the area around the garbage room.

Chief Alletto had to agree that there just wasn't enough fire damage in room 121 to have spread to other areas and completely burn all the combustibles in a hallway some eight feet away and still remain in an intact state.

I don't know too much about police work, but I do know about fires. I know that they burn up and out, leaving the point of origin and the area of origin where the worst of the complete burn is usually located. "I just can't stop investigating," I said, and Chief Alletto said "Interview this Mr. Robinson from room 121."

Mr. Robinson was scared to death-the police think he set the fire. The very first thing I asked Mr. Robinson was if a fire started in his room. "I didn't start a fire," he said "I lived there! I don't have many places that I can go to because I need to be on the first floor because of my wheel chair." This man has only one leg and is about sixty-two years old. He told me that the splice was good and had been working fine.

As I walked away I thought this guy liked living in the Paxton Hotel. Most of his friends lived there. He had no reason to burn himself out onto the street.

Chief Alletto said, "Make out your reports as to what in your opinion was the origin and cause of this fire, and get them in because the mayor wants answers. Be sure you justify and document your conclusions."

People who lived in buildings around the Paxton Hotel had reported smelling smoke about thirty-five minutes before firefighters arrived. As the huge crane chomped away the building toward the west corridor, we saw the steel that was twisted and discolored. Two more bodies were found in the middle section.

More residents are telling us that the hotel's automatic "wake-up call" system had awakened them some twenty minutes before firefighters arrived on the scene, a delay in the alarm twenty to thirty minutes. It's hard to say, but the temperature was thirty-nine degrees, with rain and twenty-mile-an-hour winds. That is not a good time to be out and about at 0330.

The city was now coming down on (SRO) single room occupancies. Mayor Richard M. Daley proposed a reexamination of all city building codes. He said we should look into the sprinkler systems because of the loss of lives. This was ridiculous—no alarms!

AREA OF ORIGIN

I started my report and determined that the area of origin was located in the west corridor between the stairway on the south and the long corridor on the north end, between the ground floor and the second floor of the subject structure.

POINT OF ORIGIN

The point of this fire's origin was, in my opinion, located in the west section of the ground floor. Approximately twenty-nine feet from the south exterior wall and twenty-three feet from the west exterior wall, and approximately three feet high from floor level along the south partitioned wall.

CAUSE OF FIRE

The point of this fire's origin indicated that area was the garbage room where two fifty-five-gallon metal drums were used for thirty-eight units to put their garbage in. This room was five foot by six foot with an eight-foot ceiling. Whatever garbage made it in the drums was one thing, but most of the time it ended up on the floor.

It is my considered opinion that this fire was an accident, based on information of how many previous alarms there were in the garbage rooms in the Paxton's history. I made this determination after a thorough fire scene examination. It is my further opinion that this fire more than likely was ignited by possibly a lit coal of a discarded cigarette into the fifty-five-gallon drums before the door was closed at 0230. The fire burned through the south wall of the garbage room and entered a pipe chase behind the slop sinks.

Once this fire was inside this wood stud and wood lath pipe chase, the fire became concealed and little, if any, smoke was showing because of the flue-like effect of the pipe chase. It is my further opinion that this fire went undetected as it burned its way up to the "cockloft" of the building.

The cockloft is the area between the ceiling of the fourth floor and the roof of the structure. In some places, the cockloft is four feet high without any obstructions. The fire filled the void with hot gases and smoke.

Fire had embers falling to the bottom of the pipe chase and fire crossed over the four-foot-nine-inch west corridor and into a pipe chase for the steam pipes that also extended to the cockloft. The fire was now roaring in the two pipe chases, the steel I beam that runs through the area of origin, and then began to conduct the heat through the steel, igniting the floor joist in the rooms south of the point of origin.

Smoke was now seen by Mr. Robinson in his bathroom ceiling and into the alcove ceiling just outside his door of room 121. Mr. Robinson fled room 121, turned north in his wheelchair where he told Mrs. Huntley, the maid, and then he fled east down the long corridor to the front door.

Within the cockloft, the fire had ignited rafters in the roof and soon burned a hole in the roof. The fire heat and gases in the cockloft re-ignited and, with a south wind at twenty miles per hour, the fire banked down the open stairways, igniting the wooden stairs and railings. With smoke on all floors, the residents were trying to escape through windows.

The Paxton Hotel residents did not become aware of this fire until it was an inferno. The opening of windows in an effort to

Author sealing an evidence can above room #121 of the Paxton Hotel.

escape also continued to give fresh air to the fire.

The building's alarm system was out of service at the time of the fire. There were no reports of anyone hearing any alarm at all early in this fire. If only one bell worked to warn one person or persons then there would not have been so many dead.

My friend, Roy Dames, from the Cook County Morgue was on the scene and said they had an ID on the arm and leg we sent them. It was inflated and they took a fingerprint, and the guy was probably three hundred pounds.

As the days passed, time and time again firefighters were praised for the outstanding rescue work that was done at the Paxton Hotel. *Chicago Sun Times* writer Raymond Coffey wrote in his column: "Thank you for your bravery and skill and professionalism, you gave us all reason to be proud. Bless you, you're great and here's to you."

The Sun Times announced every firefighter's name in the

newspaper that responded to the fire within the first hour. They wrote: "You're Pros! . . . You're Heroes! . . .We owe you!"

We continued to work on the Paxton Hotel fire for weeks after the fire. It was never directly told to me whether or not everyone was in agreement with me about the garbage room. We also collected the fifty-five-gallon drum with the hole in it, as our evidence.

About one month after the Paxton Hotel fire, a press release of the OFI report of the Paxton Hotel Fire was issued:

After an exhaustive investigation, the Chicago Fire Department, Office of Fire Investigation has completed its report on the tragic 5-11 and one special alarm fire at the Paxton Hotel, 1432 North LaSalle Street in the early morning hours of March 16, 1993.

Based upon exhaustive interviews with many employees and residents of the hotel, fire and police personnel and other witnesses, as well as intensive fire scene examination by highly trained professional fire investigators, using the most sophisticated and current fire investigation techniques, the classification of this tragic fire will remain as "exact cause unknown" at this time.

There is ample data to indicate that a delay of alarm (report of fire) was a significant factor in the spread of this fire: anywhere from five to twenty minutes after several residents and witnesses first noted smoke and heat.

Information from residents and employees of the hotel clearly indicates that a history of numerous fires went unreported to the Chicago Fire Department, and were regularly extinguished by employees and occupants of the hotel, with the use of portable fire extinguishers.

Other significant factors included the possibility of certain building construction features contributing to the fire's spread, the velocity and direction of the wind at the time of the fire, the absence of fire doors protecting the stairwells, and corridors and also pipe chases which may have allowed fire, heat, and smoke to find a convenient method of transmission into the loft area.

Information to date strongly indicates the possibility that this fire originated on upper floors at the rear west section of the hotel. More likely than not, the point of origin was in one of the garbage rooms (formerly linen rooms) of the second or third floors of the structure. Burn patterns indicated that the fire spread upward vertically through the clothes chute in the north-west corner of the garbage room, then entered the cockloft located above the ceiling of the fourth floor and under the roof of the structure.

Meanwhile, the fire began banking down into the stairwells and also horizontally through the upper corridors.

Origination of the fire in room 121 has been ruled out as a result of factors including/downward directional burn patterns, but also the following:

1. Reports of smoke and heat on upper floors by residents of some fifteen to twenty minutes prior to the discovery by persons who ultimately reported the fire.

2. Decomposition and collapse of the first-floor ceiling prior to the introduction of any water extinguishment.

3. Eyewitness reports from members of Engine 98 that the corridor ceiling on the first floor began collapsing shortly after their arrival, as well as the collapse of the center stairwell by the officer of Engine Company 98, but no actual fire on the ground floor noted.

4. Statements from the occupants of room 121 and the cleaning lady employed by the hotel at the time of the fire, indicate the fire was first witnessed on the first floor of the building.

The possibility exists that this fire may be the result of a misuse of smoking materials being emptied into the trash receptacles in one of the garbage rooms, or the intentional ignition of trash in one of the garbage receptacles.

This hypothesis is being drawn by a combination of burn patterns and the unreported track record of fires in this structure. However, since neither of these possibilities can be definitively documented at this time, the Chicago Fire Department feels the prudent thing to do is to maintain the "exact cause unknown" classification and suspend the investigation under the existing circumstances. But, should the circumstances change in any way, we would immediately initiate further investigation.

I worked the Paxton Hotel fire for some twenty-eight days and nights and we didn't have all the answers by the time the structure came down. But, all the work and hours seemed to be worth it because I know that I did everything possible to find a cause.

The bravery and sacrifice firefighters and paramedics made that morning sure made me feel good to be a firefighter. It took four hours of gruesome hard work and 250 firefighters using half the city's fire equipment to put out the 5-11 blaze.

The fire killed twenty people and injured twenty-eight and now all SROS are required to install hard-wire fire alarm systems throughout and smoke detectors in each room.

There are still many SROS in Chicago. They are called the last foothold before homelessness for many urban poor people. But remember that every citizen deserves fire protection, whether his or her home is a single room or a penthouse suite.

The last day we worked the Paxton Hotel fire was at the incinerator on Diversey, right off Ashland Avenue. The Medical Examiner's office put in hundreds of hours looking for the remains of that man, whose arm we had found. We hand-searched the remains of the Paxton Hotel in a dump behind the

FROM THE FIRE COMMISSIONER
April 28, 1993

All members of the Chicago Fire Department:

My appreciation is being extended for the expertise
performed by all members of this great fire department
on a daily basis.

I am also taking this opportunity to especially thank all
the members for their outstanding efforts extended at the
Paxton Hotel Fire, the morning of March 16, 1993, at 1432
North LaSalle Street.

The professionalism exemplified at the Paxton Hotel Fire
in the numerous recues, treatment of the injured, and subse-
quent suppression of the fire was witnessed through the
media, nationwide.

The members of the Emergency Medical Services did an
outstanding job in administering to the injured, and
carrying out their duties under such adverse conditions.

Also, a job well done by the members of the Fire Alarm
Office, for the effective dispatching and reassignment of
the numerous companies involvd on this incident.

After the fire was estinguished, a tremendous task was
placed upon our Fire Investigation Unit. A task that was
handled with the utmost professionalism.

When a crisis, such as this occurs in the city of Chicago,
the citizens of this city can be assured that the Chicago Fire
Department can be depended upon to do what they have
been trained so well to do.

The people of the city of Chicago share the great pride and
admiration that I have for our men and women on a job
well done, as in this particular incident, and other incidents
whether it be of this magnitude or of lesser extent.

Sincerely,
Raymond E. Orzco
Fire Commissioner

STATE OF ILLINOIS
EIGHTY-EIGHTH GENERAL ASSEMBLY
HOUSE OF REPRESENTATIVES
House Resolution No. 382
Offered by Representative Laurino

WHEREAS, A call of "5-11" is the most serious ranking that can be given a fire in the City of Chicago; the "5-11" sent early March 16, 1996, brought 250 fire fighters, 45 fire rigs, and 15 ambulances to the Paxton Hotel; and

WHEREAS, The first fire fighters on the scene saw residents of the single room occupancy hotel trapped on upper floors and immediately began rescues rather than trying to fight the fire; and

WHEREAS, Many unsung hereos emerged from the Paxton fire, including fire fighters, paramedics, and ambulance attendants; and

WHEREAS, Even as we join with the City of Chicago in mourning the victims of this tragic fire, we wholeheartedly give praise to the heroic efforts of the fire fighters who, without regard for their personal safety, risked their lives to save others; therefore be it

RESOLVED, BY THE HOUSE OF REPRESENTATIVES OF THE EIGHTY-EIGHTH GENERAL ASSEMBLY OF THE STATE OF ILLINOIS, that we congratulate and commend the Chicago fire fighters for their heroic actions in the Paxton Hotel fire and that we thank them for their unselfish commitment to the well-being and safety of the citizens of Chicago; and be it further

RESOLVED, That a suitable copy of this preamble and resolution be presented to Fire Commisioner Ray Orozco and the Chicago Fire Fighters Union Local 2, as an expression of our respect and admiration for all the members of the Chicago Fire Department.

Adopted by the House of Representatives on March 31, 1993.
Michael J. Madigan, Speaker of the House
Anthony D. Rossi, Clerk of the House

incinerator with Cook County K-9 dogs for three twelve-hour days. On Good Friday, April 14, the Medical Examiner called the search off.

The men and women who worked the fire were all invited back to a place on West Diversey: Eddie McFadden with Streets and Sanitation with the large payloaders that physically moved the Paxton to the incinerator; the crane operators; Hugh Heneghan who has sponsored our union Local 2 for years; the police officers from Bomb and Arson; Denny Guest and another officer from Violent Crimes; OFI; and Media Affairs, my brother Mike.

It was announced that there had been an exhaustive search for the remains of the man whose arm we found. Since there were temperatures at and above 2,000 degrees in the west corridor (where the arm was found), it was the opinion of Roy Dames that the remains of said victim were cremated in the fire.

It took days to finally get back to work on other fires and there was always one more little thing about the Paxton. On a spring morning the city of Chicago had a special awards day for the firefighters, paramedics, police, and the residents of the Paxton Hotel.

Mayor Richard M. Daley said, "Chicagoans will not forget your courageous effort in combating the Paxton Hotel blaze, and your heroic acts in rescuing its victims." Coffee was served with some sweet rolls.

A civilian walked up to me and asked why firefighters wear that unusual style helmet. I tried to explain the best I could, because this was a day when the public got to ask us about our job. I think it went like this:

THE HELMET
There is a special breed that wears this unique helmet, being

only one of its kind and having very different markings of bends, curves, and angles. This dome-shaped helmet of leather, or now plastic, has one very primary purpose. It is to protect the head from falling objects. There is a brim that is connected to the dome to protect your ears, neck and eyes. The long-shaped brim in the back of the helmet sheds water from the neck and your back.

This twisted or altered, and at times distorted, helmet is shaped with a decorative emblem type of shield. It oftentimes serves to identify that you belong to a fire company, and you are a firefighter.

Many people associate the firefighter with lungs of leather, and Dalmatian dogs as their mascots. Neither image does the fire service justice. The statistics are frightening of how many people know little or nothing about the one service dedicated to halting death and destruction from fire.

Being one of a kind, wearing this firefighter's helmet, you are a unique individual, and you belong to the "Noble Breed."

Chapter 14

THERE WERE A STACK OF UNDETERMINED FIRES THAT WERE ALREADY A week to two weeks old. It is very hard to investigate a fire that is two weeks old, because as the time of the incident begins to drift away, so do all the witnesses.

I remember what Matt said. "There is no excitement in a follow-up investigation compared to a working still and box alarm where you have firefighters working and all the victims and witnesses are still on the scene."

Early one Sunday evening, April 25, 1993, a still alarm was given to Engines 55 and 112, and Trucks 44 and 28 at 1818. The fire was located at 1801 West Diversey in a vacant three-story mill constructed structure. Extra alarms were pulled as the fire escalated, and just when the firefighters thought they had a handle on the fire, smoke began rolling off the top floor of a six-story brick storage building and within one hour the fire escalated to a 5-11 and one special alarm.

Two 5-11 alarms in less than a month! Commissioner Orozco was again testing the equipment of the Chicago Fire Department. Not to say anything about the firefighters who were stretching lines for over two blocks. My pager goes off and it's the Fire

State Police Officer Mitch Kushner and K-9 dog Nikki.

Alarm Office: by orders of Chief Pat Burns, he wants me to respond from home to the 5-11 and one special alarm.

There was one big difference to this 5-11, there were no victims. I was assigned the case by Pat Burns and remained on the scene until 1400 the next day. The work load was getting heavy again.

As the months went on, I talked to Chief Alletto about getting my license to investigate fires, because when I reached the age of fifty years old, I wanted to retire. But if I chose, I could continue investigating fires in the private sector. Chief Alletto thought that my obtaining a license was a good idea. Chief Alletto said, "Go for it, Cos."

I had just returned from Collinsville, Illinois, with Jack

Lumsden and Joe Gruszka. We attended a seminar on "Fire and Arson." I enjoyed the seminar, and learned a lot. The certificates were starting to add up, and my resume was looking better every day. I joined the International Association of Arson Investigators. In the month of May, I made an interviewing seminar, and a bomb scene investigation seminar with my good friends Jack Malooly and John Maroca from ATF, who were giving the class.

The summer months were hot, and it was very uncomfortable working days in a hot office all day. I was out getting lunch when I heard that we were going to see and meet the state fire marshal's K-9 dog Nikki, and also his handler, Mitch Kushner. Mitch is a state fire investigator who now investigates fires with his dog. He is a certified accelerant detection canine handler. They trained together as a team in 1992, at the main state police arson K-9 school.

When we were looking for accelerants in a fire scene, we used an electronic tool called a "sniffer." This was designed to detect accelerants. I never thought much of it. Matt said, "It makes a buzzing sound when it detects a little evidence, but I wouldn't go into court with just the evidence that it went off."

Mitch enlightened us with a little history on Nikki. Dogs have a keen sense of smell and are able to detect substances which humans and sophisticated equipment cannot. He played a game where he puts one drop of gasoline on someone's shoe and when everyone lines up, the dog walked right to the gasoline and sat down, which is the signal that he has found an accelerant.

Nikki will be called before I ever use the sniffer again. Dogs can detect a substance of which the concentration is one part per trillion in the atmosphere. However, this is merely another tool. If utilized properly, before requesting a K-9 arson dog, I must have a good indication that accelerants may be present, i.e., burn or pour patterns, etc.

One hot afternoon at 1335, a still alarm was given to Engines 4 and 22, Trucks 10 and 3, Squad 1 and the Third Battalion chief. The fire was located at 1510 North Dearborn. Upon the arrival of Engine 4 there was heavy smoke pouring out of the rear of the building on the west side. A still and box alarm was requested.

This day, Fire Commissioner Raymond Orozco was just coming out of the Merchandise Mart when he heard Engine 4 request the box. He started moving in the direction of the fire. With all the talk about occupants still in the building he took the fire in, and upon his arrival ordered a 2-11 alarm. There was no gangway on the block, and the alley was too small to back an engine down. There is only one way to get to the seat of this fire, and that is the hard work of firefighters.

The fire commissioner requested a 3-11 alarm. The street is very narrow, one way north and filled with trees. It was going to be very hard to get water back and up to the top of this building.

Truck 10 broke a few tree branches and finally set the one-hundred-foot tower ladder on the coping of the fire building in an effort to ventilate the roof. Engine 4 began a lead out that will have to make about thirty-five feet to the fire building, and up three flights of stairs through a door, and now a sixty-five-foot hallway before they can get to the seat of this fire. It's a tough lead out!

Squad 1 and Truck 3 laddered the front of the occupied burning building. In the rear, Lieutenant Joe Klem and his crew of Engine 98 also had one hell of a lead out themselves. From Clark Street to the rear of the structure was a very small fire escape. However, it was their only access to the rear. They stretched their two-and-a-half-inch hand line up the very narrow fire escape to the third floor, where they entered through a bedroom window, and over the bed and out to the hall and up a small set of stairs to the fire floor!

The firefighters now had completed their primary search.

The fire was now vented through the roof of this four-story brick constructed building. The Main Fire Alarm operator called me on the radio and said, "Take in the 3-11 on Dearborn by orders of 4-6-1 Burns." Now as I am responding, I am thinking that I have spent more time with Pat Burns than I have with my wife these last few months.

It was a sunny day and the wind was out of the south at about ten miles per hour, and the heavy black smoke fell across Lincoln Park. I parked the black sedan about a block away and started south toward the fire. I haven't been to a working fire in a while. I found Pat Burns. He told me that Tony Rodriguez had the fire, but the Englewood Fire Alarm Office needed an OFI car, and he told Tony that "Cos will respond here and you take the fire on the South Side."

They're all in there hitting fire now, because white and gray smoke is flowing out of the burned-out roof. It was very hot. The temperature was eight-eight degrees and the humidity was a bitch, which causes the smoke to just hang close.

Ben Gariti was the chief of the First District, and had been here since the box alarm. He informed me that most of the fire was in the rear on the south side. The excitement was just too much for me. I had to go into the fire building. I told Burns that I was going to look around, and he said "Don't get lost."

I climbed up to the fourth floor. There was a room on the southwest side that had completely burned out, and showed signs of flashover. The faces of these young new firefighters, all dirty from the soot and smoke, with Self Contained Breathing Apparatus SCBA face-pieces pulled to one side, had a tough go, but they were tenacious and won!

I met Pat Burns and told him that this fire originated in room 407, and he found out that the occupant was evicted just this morning.

We had to check up on this lead right now, and started asking questions. Sure enough, a woman who occupied 407 was evicted today, but no one had seen or heard from her in many days. I checked with the owner, who discovered the fire. He said he did have to evict the woman in apartment 407 for a problem with the rent. I asked him to stay around. I needed to talk to him later.

A newspaper reporter nudged me and asked if we had a cause. I told him we won't have one for about a week. This same reporter said, "Hey were you just in that fire?" In the same breath, the same reporter asked if I could tell him what it is like being inside a fire building. I stopped dead in my tracks. "What's it like to be in a fire?" I looked at him and said, "There is nothing like it. There is a door from the burning apartment into this hallway that has been opened. The intense heat of about 1400 to 1600 degrees is above your head with heavy smoke backing down on top of you as you slowly move forward with the line. If you don't have a mask on or you have taken it off at this time your bronchial tubes will begin to get scorched, along with your lungs, and your throat will begin to close and you will begin coughing and choking." I walked away from the reporter.

Most of the fire was out and engines were picking up their lines. Pat Burns and a couple of chiefs and myself returned to the fourth floor. Cinders were still falling as we entered 407. The witness said the fire was right in front of the kitchen door.

With some help from the firefighters we dug out a section of clothes and papers until we reached the wood floor. Sure enough there was a large burn pattern on the wood floor right by the kitchen door. Water was cascading down the front marble stairwell as we were leaving and all of a sudden Pat Burns slipped on the west marble steps and his feet went up and his ass went down. Now Pat is a big guy, about six foot six, 285 pounds. You just knew he had a big "pain in the ass"!

I saw the look in his eye that he got hurt. He said, "Help me out of this water." I knew I couldn't do it myself, and I yelled for help, because I knew Pat was too heavy for me to lift alone. He was put on a stretcher and transported to Northwestern Hospital by Ambulance 11.

Again, I am here alone on another major fire. I conducted a cursory investigation and told the owner I would return. The investigation went on for about three days until I determined that a janitor had discarded a cigarette while cleaning out the vacant apartment. The woman who had been evicted, who now lives in Valparaiso, Indiana, did not start the fire.

Pat Burns was X-rayed and released from the hospital with instructions to get bed rest for one week. The excitement of responding to fires was great, and I wanted more of it. All I see is burned-out buildings with a hundred questions to be found, and it is a great feeling when you get the questions answered.

At the end of August, they came out with a new directive about the method for recording emergency response activities. It's called the National Fire Incident Reporting System (NFIRS).It is now the primary method for recording Chicago Fire Department fire calls. Also, the city authorized personal flash-lights. These were to be issued to all suppression and field oper-ations personnel. Hey, that's me, I think! In the very next direc-tive, there was a department policy for lost or stolen or damaged equipment like flashlights, etc.

As Pat enters, he says "All right, Marshals, who's up?"

"I am," I said. Pat informed me that the fire was a 3-11 alarm last night, and he needs a marshal on it this morning. Okay, I told him, it's mine. The address was 1225-27 West School Street. It was hot and muggy. We were given pullover work clothes for work-ing on a hot day.

Around noon, a car pulled up in front of this badly burned-out structure, and a woman got out and began crying. I came outside because anyone who cries like that knows a lot about the building. I introduced myself to her as the investigating fire marshal, and asked a few basic questions. As she calmed down, she told me her name was Suzanne Plunkett and she rented some storage space from John, the person who touches up photos. Mrs. Plunkett also informed me that all or most of the businesses at this location were into the arts. Plunkettt said all her negatives were in file cabinets downstairs and that she was a photographer.

I informed her that there was no way she could go down there. She continued saying that she has to go in there to get her things and she will just wait until I leave. I went down the stairs to take a look. It is about a fifty-foot hallway just before the area where there was total collapse. The worst part of being in this hallway was that the water was about two inches below the top of my hip boots. Mrs. Plunkett gave me the key to her storage room and told me that all the money she has is in a manila folder next to her desk and begged me to find it.

As I was wading through this high standing water again, I asked myself why I always get involved with people.

I unlocked the door and very carefully made my way over toward the desk. It was almost totally under water. I reached down in between the desk and a file cabinet and there was the manila folder with about $1,000 inside. Part of the money was burned but most of it was there. When I handed the money to Mrs. Plunkett, she was so happy, and it made me feel good, too.

Suzanne Plunkett thanked me and left with her brother, and I continued with my investigation. About a month later, I received a thank you from her. She told me she had a new studio at 3047 North Lincoln. If I ever needed any photographic work or retouch of photos, to please give her a call.

As I remember, I was only four years old when my father died, a Chicago Fire Department lieutenant. There were no photos of him anywhere. I believe my mother told me that "he didn't like being in front of a camera." One day, my sister Kathy called me and said one of her girlfriends found a photo of a baseball team at the University of Chicago and that our father's name is right next to the team's photo.

Sure enough, it was a picture of my father. They had a few copies made of the team photograph. One day I visited Suzanne Plunkett to show her the photo of the team. She suggested since my father is on the very end she might be able to take him out of the photo and make an individual photo from it.

Not only did Suzanne Plunkett take my father out of the team photo, but she retouched the background so that it looked like he was in the photo himself. It was a great gift from Suzanne, and I won't forget it ever! Now, after forty-eight years, I have a picture of my father. Fire investigation is good, but I miss the fires, like Matt said. One follow-up after the next, they just become routine. But, I said to myself, "Bill, you're doing very important work, and don't ever forget that."

One of the investigators on the second platoon, Mike Cucci, had told me on a couple of occasions that he might want to get on the day group, and he asked me if I wanted to trade. He would go on days and I would go back into a twenty-four-hour car. I thought the only problem I would have, is Alletto. I made him an offer he couldn't refuse. He knew I wanted to get back on track and I had determined to learn all there is to know about the business.

In November, I attended a Youthful Fire Setter Seminar. It was only a sixteen-hour class, but the information overwhelmed me and the statistics frightened me.

Statistics show that 40 percent of those arrested for arson

are under the age of eighteen years old. Just think about field fires, dumpster and trash fires, and even garage fires. In most cases, these fires are not accidental. During the late '80s, juvenile fire setting ranked fifth among causes of home fire deaths. The largest ignition source for juveniles are matches, lighters and candles. For some reason, these ignition sources will probably remain accessible to children in the foreseeable future. Unless there is a way to educate the parents and the children that it is a must to keep children away from fire, we will always have these statistics until more people get involved and identify this problem.

Well, I tried. A memo went out to the battalion chiefs in the field that if any fire is set by a youth, to get a copy of the NIFRS to Bill Cosgrove. Within a week I had forty fire reports on my desk.   I tried to get the youthful fire setters' position organized in the Chicago Fire Department, but in order to help these kids you need manpower. There was no available manpower in OFI, and we still had a shortage of marshals. That's when I knew that the forty or so follow-ups on youthful fire setters were going to have to wait for a while.

A new fresh class of firefighters was almost finished with all of their training at the Fire Academy. I paid close attention to this academy class, because one of my daughter's very good friends was in this class. Not only were John and Candice Patton friends of my daughter, Tracy, they were both in my daughter's wedding party.

The news traveled fast that day on November 25, 1993 that while in a training exercise, candidate Steven McNamee was killed while jumping into an airbag from the roof of the academy. Just the weekend before, John Patton and other candidates helped Steve and his wife Maryrose and their two children move into a new home on Chicago's southwest side. It happened

almost at the end of their training. They were part of Group 5 and
Steven McNamee had already ordered a plaque for his instruc-
tors from Group 5 at Gene Furmaneck's store, G & L Fire Gifts at
111th and Pulaski.

Now, on a very sunny day, firefighters from all around our
nation, together with their brothers from Chicago, paid tribute to
a fallen comrade. As the casket was ever so carefully lifted up
onto the pumper, the hundreds of firefighters stood at attention
and snapped a full white-gloved salute.

By the time the new year rolled around, I had 120 follow-up
youthful fire setters to call back. But that had nothing to do with
the two fire follow-ups that I was working on, and the three more
that sat on my desk. The fire department had just come out with
how many runs there were last month. There had been 3,733 still
alarms, and 3,413 ambulance assists runs, also in the last month.
The ambulance assistance program has more rules every day,
and the newest one was when the closest ambulance company is
on assignment, then the closest available ambulance assistance
unit will be dispatched. The Chicago Fire Department is always
changing, and it is clear today that this ambulance assistance program is here to stay. Firefighters don't like it much, but EMS has
been given a high priority in the fire department.

There was a lot of talk about not working under a contract for
over two years. There were rumors about the contract from the
steward's meeting. One of the first things was that whatever pay
raise we did get, all this would be retro pay back to January 1,
1992 because the last contract ran out on December 31, 1991.

Also, there was a lot of talk about the paramedics going on
eight-hour shifts, but it was only a rumor. I was very optimistic
about the contract as I thought our executive board would get the
best package available. I hoped the membership would just
remain calm.

Finally, in February Mike Cucci and I changed shifts. It was winter, but I felt good about going back on the twenty-four-hour response group. Being on the day shift, I had learned a lot about fires and fire investigation. To be a lead investigator on a fire like the Paxton Hotel, I had a chance to complete an in-depth investigation report. Although the real cause did not come out, my theory of what occurred still remained the most logical explanation of what took place at that hotel on March 16, 1993.

I walked into Engine 44's quarters at 412 North Kedzie. Our offices are downstairs in the lower level. There was a small TV room with a round table and a sofa along the wall. The other room was where all the computer equipment was located, for report writing. Up until now, I had not used the computer to complete an incident report. But I was willing to learn-whether I liked it or not, this is a computerized world, and you must learn it to remain competitive. It is a great marketable skill.

I was working with Tony Rodriguez, a young lieutenant who is a great guy. He said, "You're up for the next run and you're in 4-6-3 today, Cos. There are only two of us today." I made my bunk. There were just two rooms to clean and a bathroom and that was the extent of the housework.

The only problem with this trade was now I was on the second shift and for over twenty-five years I had always been on the first platoon. I was in the red and black sedan when I got my first run.

"Main to 4-6-3, meet the Ninth Battalion at 1325 West Touhy." Being from the South Side, I asked myself, "is that the fucking city?" With my lights and siren on, I was back to my real element once again. I still get very excited going to a fire scene and to see what amazing moment or challenge will be around the next corner for me.

I arrived on the scene, and the fire was out, but you could see the first-floor windows had been broken out by the firefighters. Bob Devens is the chief of the Ninth Battalion, and a friend. We worked as firefighters together at Engine 45 and Truck 15 in the old days.

Chief Devens informed me that upon his arrival on the scene there was a little smoke emanating from these first-floor windows, and he pointed toward them. The concerned structure is a three-story brick courtyard type structure, with exterior dimensions of approximately 150 by 300 by 30 feet.

As we were walking into the apartment, Devens was telling me that we didn't have to lead out. We knocked the fire down with hand pumps. On my way in, a woman who lives in the building said that they had domestic difficulties with the young couple in that apartment. I thanked her for that information, and I see two paramedics are working on this young guy who has burns on the front of his legs and he is ranting and raving about how you can't make him go to the hospital.

There were a few of the firefighters from Truck Company 25 standing with tools in hand, waiting for the chief to tell them to pick up.

I looked around the apartment casually and noted that there had been two fires. One in the living room and another in the kitchen. There was a can, and the place smelled like kerosene. I leaned over to this young boy sitting in the chair and said, "What did you do here, sir?" He started to say something and I yelled back, "You'd better go to the hospital son, because I think when the police get here you sure will go with them!" "Sure, get real," he said to me. I leaned over him again and said, "Son, this is as real as it gets," pointing to the fire against the wall.

I thanked Devens and the firefighters for their efficient work, and Devens looks back and says, "Cos will stroke you." Ha ha. The young boy has now decided to go to the hospital with the good paramedics. We're taking him to Saint Francis Hospital in Evanston, Marshal." The witness said that after hearing glass breaking, she looked out of her third-floor door, and there was smoke in the hallway and she called 9-1-1. Within the first-floor apartment, I found a one-gallon metal can with some liquid inside. There were clothes and paper piled against the wall in the living room. The fire was out, with just a small amount of damage.

The other fire was located in the kitchen next to the stove. This fire was a little larger and burned up to the cabinets in the kitchen.

Number one rule: it is almost impossible to have two fires in two different rooms where there is no means of communication between them. These were deliberately set fires. I called for Bomb and Arson, and an evidence technician. Then I needed to check the natural gas, electrical system and the furnace.

After inspecting them, I eliminated them as factors. I remanded custody of the scene to the Beat Patrol Officer, who would wait for the Bomb and Arson Detectives.

I made a small sketch, and took twenty-four photos. I left for Saint Francis Hospital in Evanston, to get a statement from this kid who apparently set the fire in this apartment. This young boy said that his girlfriend was in his house with some guy when he got home from work, and she set the fire. "Oh," I asked, "How did you get burned?" He was angry with me. He tried to tell me that she loved him and only him. He was talking and I stopped him. I told him that he definitely thought too much of himself! "If you think that your unrelated mishaps in life are worth my valuable time, they are not. If you have anyone to be angry at, it should be yourself. You set this fire and you will have to face it, young man."

I returned by way of Sheridan Road, which is alongside of Lake Michigan. It was a blustery day in February, and the waves from the lake were splashing heavily against the shoreline. I already had a fire under my belt and it was only noon. It looked like this might be a "rock and roll" twenty-four hours!

As the days went by, Mike Deckelmann helped me with the computer and showed me how to work with the program. Typing was different, but not too bad. After I learned a little more with the computer, I got real good, because of how many fires I got. However, I still used two fingers to type, but so what. Chief Alletto types forty words per minute on the computer with four fingers.

I talked to Chief Alletto and told him I wanted to get my own license to investigate fires. Chief Alletto was excited that I wanted to get the license. He told me that I would have to call the Illinois Department of Professional Regulation for an application. I received the package by mail and it took about three hours to fill out all of the information about my life. In order to take this examination, you must have been actively involved with investigation work and have at least two of the last five years in the investigation business.

I filled out all the forms and bought all the books that I needed to study. I began to study and work my twenty-four hours. My Daley day was great, five days off in a row. It felt so good to be back on the 24-hour platoon.

Chapter 15

As winter turned into spring, I began to like the second shift. There was always this thing about the other shifts on this job, that they weren't as good as the first shift. If anything proved wrong, it was that theory, because I watched them, the firefighters in the first, second and third platoons. All were hard, tough workers. I took as much work as I could, and studied for the upcoming Private Detective exam in September.

One night I had returned from a run, and all of the rigs were home. I took a look around at this newer type firehouse. The overhead fluorescent lights on the apparatus floor highlighted the rigs. On the north side of this four-bay-door firehouse were four spare ambulances and in front of the ambulances were the three red and black OFI sedans. They were finally good cars and not shop rejects. Chief Alletto was finally able to get us some decent cars.

Truck 36 was a big rig with compartments all around. On top sat a one-hundred-foot aerial ladder with a nozzle affixed to the top of the ladder. Jump seats contained the gear of the firefighters all ready to go. In the first bay of this firehouse was Engine 44, and it was always my understanding that the house belonged to

Engine Company #44s Fire House O.F.I. Black and Red Sedans.

the engine company and all the other apparatus were merely "visitors."

This super-sized pumper looked so big to me because it wasn't long ago that we worked with smaller engines and they looked our size. The hose bed is so high you have to bend your neck, but now there is a bed of new hose called large diameter hose, four- or five-inch. While the engine remains in front of a fire building, the officer has an option of using the deck gun or a lead out of the one-and-three-fourths-inch cross bay bed. I just wonder to myself what my friends (the old timers) would say about all this fancy equipment. It would sound like this, "You may ride a more modern apparatus, learn new fire suppression techniques, enjoy shorter hours and more pay, but a firefighter must always live in a world of smoke, flames, and falling walls. If you do not truly like this kind of work, you will never be happy, and will end up a "ducker."

The speaker opens throughout this firehouse, and the dispatcher yells, "Engines 44 and 57, Trucks 7 and 10 you have a fire at 2119 West Fulton." As the firefighters scramble for their places, the loud engines start up. A cloud of smoke now fills the air as the doors begin to go up and they are gone, a really fast push out. I closed the doors of the firehouse and my portable radio crackles "Engine 44 to Main, we have a working fire."

Bobby Hoff is in the Sixth Battalion, and has requested a box alarm as soon as he pulls up. "Battalion Six to Main, one-story truss-roofed industrial type building." I responded on the box alarm and was there in a matter of three minutes. Fire was belching out of the roof in the rear of the building. Engine Company 44 dropped two lines. They led the two-and-a-half-inch line around the side of the structure and then the first of three explosions occurred from cylinders of compressed gas. The explosions pushed out the wall and the one-story truss roof fell in and a ball of flames went one hundred feet into the sky!

Deputy District Chief Bill Nolan requested a 2-11 alarm fire, and they surrounded the fire and started pouring the water on it.

I don't like explosions. They scare the hell out of me. The company, General Surface Hardening, had been in full operation. The operator of an overhead crane was removing a skid of metal from the furnace, when it got hung up on a door. At this time, the skid started to tip to one side dropping part of the skid into a vat of oil splashing hot oil up onto the furnace. This then erupted into a ball of fire. The fire was an accident, but a three-hour OFI incident report had to be completed by morning, since Fire Commissioner Orozco would be looking for it.

The next membership application I filled out was the National Association of Fire Investigators, and I attended their Fire and Explosion certification program. I studied for the examination and passed, though it was a hard first day of class. The new fire and explosion certificates brought me up to about twelve, and the resume continued to build.

I was assigned to take the private detectives' examination in Skokie. The test was very difficult. There were only about four or five questions about fire and arson. The rest of the examination was about police work, guns and drugs, and topics that I had no interest in whatsoever!

At this time, three of the Chicago Fire Department's engine companies celebrated one hundred years of service to this city. I wondered what it was like back then. I think they all had small wooden two-story one-bay type firehouses about 25 by 60 feet in length. I am sure that in 1893, they were all horse-drawn steamers pulled by two beautiful black horses. Between the three steamers, they could pump 400 to 550 gallons per minute and were probably Ahrens and or Columbian type.

We know what we have to do to get ready to respond to a fire today. I just couldn't imagine having to hitch the horses, then get my hat, coat, and boots on. Just think about it. Those guys really broke their asses.

Well, we finally got our new contract on September 30, 1994, about two-and-a-half years late, but we did get it. A raise in salary of about 13 percent with full retroactivity for all salaries and salary related items. I guess the biggest thing in the contract was the changing of the hours for paramedics to twenty-four hours on duty followed by seventy-two hours off duty with Daley days eliminated.

We got an increase in our clothing allowance by $175 per year. We were able to protect our minimum manning clause of five persons on all engines and trucks. This contract only lasted until June 30, 1995 and the members of this executive board would be right back at the bargaining table in the next couple of months. A contract is a contract, and we might not get everything we want, but we will always get something good for us. There is a method to our strategy, keep building the contract.

Pat Burns is coming down hard on some of the marshals, and since there is no overtime for report writing, we have all fallen a few behind. The new memo from the big office on Thirty-first Street is when time constraints prohibit the completion of an incident report, you absolutely must prepare the notification form with any information regarding the fire. It seems that some of the marshals are going home on a Daley day and information was needed downtown and in the Fire Prevention Bureau. More often, Bomb and Arson Detectives were looking for information on an arrest to be made.

Also, a new fire investigation classification memo had just been written for all OFI personnel:

In the hope of making some legal clarification, the following procedure shall be strictly adhered to: Whenever a fire is the result of some direct or deliberate human action, the fire shall be classified as incendiary, unless mitigating circumstances are present.

By this, it is meant that if someone uses a cigarette lighter, a match or deliberately lights a piece of paper with the pilot light or burner of a stove and a fire occurs, this is a deliberate and direct human action, and the fire shall be classified as incendiary. The same shall apply with the deliberate ignition of pyrotechnics (fireworks).

Whether or not there is any criminal culpability is something that will be determined by the circumstances surrounding the fire. Incendiary, as you all know, can be criminal or non-criminal. All incendiary fires are not arson. All arson fires, though, are incendiary.

As an example, if someone is using smoking materials and is under the influence of intoxicating liquor, illegal drugs, or the effects of legal drugs [prescribed medicine], or the person falls asleep, there is no incendiary condition, since the human action was to smoke a cigarette, and there was no intention of causing any fire damage.

If a child is unsupervised or unattended, and is playing with matches under the age of seven, [use of reason factor] this incident is incendiary but the person cannot be held in any way accountable, [although the parents or guardians may have some liability]. This scenario will call for an "accidental" classification. If the unsupervised or unattended child utilized an open flame, i.e., matches, cigarette lighter, gas burners on a cooking stove, for the purpose of keeping warm or for cooking, then the mitigating circumstances here would indicate an accidental ignition also.

Where someone over age seven would utilize a cigarette or cigar, etc., to deliberately set a fire, then this would certainly be an incendiary fire, and in all probability, a criminally set fire.

Remember, the deliberateness of the act and factors of aggravation or mitigation determine whether or not an incendiary act is criminal or non-criminal.

Until recently, most insurance companies did not take arson very seriously. They would just say it was a garage fire, but now it's a garage fire with a Corvette and a new Cadillac, and somewhere in the $100,000 game. They realized that arson was very hard to prove in court. Experts say arson accounts for 15 to 30 percent or more of all building fires.

After the fire is extinguished the question always asked is, where and how did this fire start? One of the first steps in determining the origin is found by studying burn patterns, and the lowest point of burning in the area of origin. The point of origin can also indicate evidence of possible arson. If two points of origin are found in two separate and distinct places, then in all probability, you have an arson on your hands.

Even though you're thinking very strong about arson, you must not assume it was arson. You must rule out all other possible accidental or natural causes, before establishing the incendiary condition. You may continue on the assumption of arson, but it is imperative to eliminate all other causes of the fire before making an incendiary classification.

To recognize that a fire was arson, you would need to know something about setting fires and the methods that are used.

The simplest of all is just paper and a few matches, but then there are mechanisms that consist of an ignition device and a timer, etc. Trailers are often used along with gasoline and kerosene, which will spread and intensify the fire.

We collect our samples, and put the evidence in air tight containers for later analysis. We interview witnesses, occupants, firefighters, and chiefs to familiarize ourselves with the situation. We are brought up to date by the chief as soon as possible. The complete interior must be photographed and the exterior of every fire. Film is cheap so document everything.

The report must be as factual as can be, and explained in a concise and clear manner. Short sentences make a report easier to read and easier to check for pertinent facts. The reports are easier to type now and most of the marshals are getting to be very creative writers. Matt would be proud!

Then I received a letter from the Department of Professional Regulations. I did not pass the Private Detectives' examination. I was so fucking mad at myself, and the exam had cost $210! I never did very well testing. That's probably one of the reasons I never got promoted. I can take the next Private Detective's test in March, but this time I will be ready.

Every year, Fire Prevention Week commemorates the anniversary of the Great Chicago Fire. Soon we were commemorating the 123rd anniversary. It is a time when the city of Chicago honors their firefighters for bravery and heroic acts above and beyond the call of duty. A memorial service is held at the Roseville Cemetery honoring all the deceased members of the past year. This event is sponsored by the Ladies Auxiliary to the Chicago Firefighters' Union Local 2. Citizens of Chicago are urged to use smoke detectors and also to visit their local firehouse, and become acquainted with their firefighters.

A very early fire occurred at Kitzel's Pickle Company, located at 837 North California, and the Main Fire Alarm Office gave the still alarm to Engines 26 and 30 and Trucks 7 and 36 and the Sixth Battalion.

Upon the arrival of Battalion Six on the scene, Chief Porter requested a still and box alarm fire. He gave the Main Fire Alarm Office a description of a two-story brick, and in the center, a one-story truss-roofed manufacturing company. Porter further stated that he had fire on the second floor, and the scene looked to have been the result of an explosion.

I responded right behind Engine 44 because they too were taking in the still and box alarm. The exterior of the structure was approximately 500 by 125 feet and there was a heavy odor in the air similar to ammonia. The structure was heavily damaged on the east exterior, and the south exterior walls were blown outward causing bricks to be thrown fifty feet from the structure and onto the street. Two large fires were burning out of control on the second floor. Ed Porter ordered Truck 36 to extend their aerial ladder and take a two-and-a-half-inch line up the aerial ladder to fight the fire. The structure with the one-story brick with the truss roof had the trusses blown off their supporting walls. Squad 2 raised their snorkel and with a four-inch line from Engine 44, extinguished the fire on the west side of the building.

We entered the structure very cautiously from the front. The ammonia was so strong, I wasn't able to enter the building until the firefighters secured the ammonia leak.

Deputy District Chief Mike Murphy 2-2-4 requested 5-1-1 the Chicago Fire Department's Hazardous Materials Unit while the fire was being contained. It was determined that the ammonia was leaking from a coil in a cooler in the center area of the structure. The haz-mat team of firefighters were able to locate the leak, and contain it in the cooler. The firefighters extinguished the fire and I began my fire/explosion scene examination.

The anhydrous ammonia, after leaking from a large coil in the ground floor cooler, then exited out a conveyer belt opening. This allowed the gas to escape into an open stairway to the second-floor offices. Anhydrous ammonia has a vapor density of .06, which is lighter than air, which has a vapor density of 1.0, and because the gas is lighter than air, it began to rise upward into the rooms of the second floor of the concerned structure.

This escaping gas collected in the second floor and the cockloft between the ceiling and the roof of the second floor. From interviewing workers of the company, it was learned that the odor of ammonia had been heavy for about an hour before the explosion. They are very used to the smell of ammonia in the company, and didn't think too much of it.

The offices of the company on the second floor did not open until 0800. Mounted on the wall in the office was a set back thermostat that called for heat, and the gas forced-air furnace ignited, and so did the anhydrous ammonia. I learned a rule of thumb: if a gas or flammable/combustible will stay in the liquid form out in the air, it is usually heavier than air.

The fire was extinguished and we all returned to our quarters. It was after 0800, so the report would have to wait until next day.

The city of Chicago approved on March 1, 1994 that all class

A single family buildings should have at least one carbon monoxide detector installed within forty feet of all rooms used for sleeping. The fire department issued a carbon monoxide meter to each company designated as a meter company.

Carbon monoxide is an odorless, tasteless, colorless gas that is deadly. It is the by-product of a fuel-burning process. The survey of the premises will determine if there are any amounts above nine parts per million of carbon monoxide present.

Well, in the month of November, the fire trucks that had been designated as meter companies had been getting between eighteen to twenty calls a day! They are called C.O. runs, and these fire companies were running their asses off, trying to keep up with the number of calls we received.

The Chicago Fire Department is now responding to so many different types of calls other than fires. Remember not to let your guard down, always protect yourself. All of these runs are dangerous to us-if there is a reading of thirty-five parts per million of carbon monoxide, put your self-contained breathing apparatus on before you say later that you're sick.

When you return from a C.O. run or a haz-mat incident, check your gear to make sure that there are no odors of gases that can make you sick. If the incident was bad, rinse off your gear with water and clean your mask thoroughly.

The cold weather was setting in again and it was time to get our cold weather gear out. This is another time to take extra care of yourself. Stay safe. But this was my last day before my annual furlough began, and I would be off duty for the holidays. It became a very busy day for OFI. We had seven runs by 2200, but my interest was in getting all of my reports completed before my furlough began. At 0247, Engines 70 and 59, Trucks 47 and 25 and the Ninth Battalion were given a still alarm of fire at 1528 West Rosemont. This was right across the street from Engine 70's firehouse and they were on the scene in a minute.

Chief Devens reported a fire on the second floor of an occupied building, and he requested a still and box alarm. The structure involved was a three-story brick building with outside dimensions of 50 by 75 feet. Engines 70 and 59 led out hose through the front and up to the second-floor apartment. Truck 47 opened the roof while other firefighters rescued people from the burning structure. The fire originated on a buffet in the dining room.

The occupant stated that she had a Christmas centerpiece made of tree branches and pine cones on the buffet. She had two candles on either side of the centerpiece. She had been sitting on her sofa when she smelled smoke. She tried to extinguish the blaze, but could not and was burned on her hands, arms and face. She was taken to Edgewater Hospital along with a woman from the third floor, by Ambulance 31.

As the firefighters from the Ninth Battalion fought the fire, I began interviewing the other tenants who had safely evacuated the burning building. One man told me that there were no smoke detectors in the building, and I began looking for evidence of this fact. The firefighters did not hear any alarms nor any smoke detectors. I asked a woman whom I thought was the owner about the detectors. She told me she was not the owner, but the owner was a Vietnamese and could not speak English. Well, I told her that she better tell him that he has no smoke detectors in the building, and the law requires them, and that they be kept in good working order!

At this time, the Vietnamese guy starts to get up in my face about how there are smoke detectors everywhere in the building. I said to the woman "No speak? He seems to understand now!"

This guy continued yelling at me about fire, and how tenants took down the smoke detectors. I asked a police officer to kindly assist me with this guy, but now I am pissed-off. A report came back from the hospital that the woman they rescued from the third floor had died of smoke inhalation.

The fire was basically out and the firefighters were taking down ladders and rolling up their hoses. I was talking to Bob Devens, the chief of the Ninth Battalion, when we noticed smoke emanating from the baseboard on the third floor. I told Devens that was smoke but he said no, he thought it was steam. In the meantime, the owner is up on the stairs. I told him he can't be in the building until we are finished. The smoke continued to fill the floor up and Chief Devens called Engine 70 on the radio to tell them to bring the line back up, we had a little rekindle in the hall. All of a sudden, this little Vietnamese guy starts calling us "motherfuckers" and yelling about who pays for this mistake saying, "I will sue you motherfuckers." I didn't have time to see which firefighter it was who pushed him into the wall, and told him to shut the fuck up.

I called the police officer up into the building, and told him that this guy was interfering with the firefighters doing their job. The officer said "Sir . . ." and the Vietnamese guy called him a motherfucker, too. That was a big mistake, because in one second he was lying on the floor in two inches of water, face down with the police officer's foot on his back.

Not only did this building not have smoke detectors, there were no carbon monoxide detectors in the structure. I made sure that all the code violations were submitted to the Fire Prevention Bureau.

I always liked being off duty at Christmas time, and being home with my wife and kids.

The examination for the private detectives was going to be in March and I started once again to study. In order to investigate fires in the state of Illinois, you must have a Private Detective's license.

Most of the questions that were asked were from the Private Detective, Private Alarm and Private Security Act of 1983. I had to study the Illinois Criminal Law and Procedures, and a book about criminal investigation. Also, the Constitution of the United States and the Illinois Constitution, and a handbook of government.

It is very hard to read and remember things like bills of attainder, ex post facto laws, and writs of habeas corpus. I am a firefighter and now a fire investigator and this test is bullshit. There are no more than four questions on fires on this examination, and I thought to myself that some people in the private detective business want to keep us out of fire investigation for their own selfish purposes.

For lawyers and some of the courts, fire investigation is called "junk science." That's because they really don't know anything about fire investigation. It is an "art" acquired through actual firefighting experience. We all know that fire burns up and out. It's the scientific principle we all learned in school, but with me, it was a little later. This type of science is a process that begins with a purpose to answer questions of why, when and how. Then a procedure is followed, so you can make some observations. Finally, your scientific method will reach a conclusion. It is, however, not an exact science, it is an art. Trying to make it a pure science is a mistake of the first magnitude!

The National Fire Protection Associations 921, is a guide for fire investigators that is based on accepted scientific principles, so that we as fire investigators can render an opinion as to the cause, origin, responsibility, and the prevention of future fires and explosion incidents. Yes, scientific principles are used, but cannot be used exclusively. Firefighting experience, and principles of fire prevention must also be relied upon. This science and the art of fire investigation, is obtained through fire experience of years on the job and also through training and education.

Chapter 16

THE MONTH OF JANUARY STARTED OUT VERY BUSY AND COLD. ON January 10, 1995 at 1015, a still alarm was given to Engines 61 and 50, Trucks 30 and 37 and the Seventeenth Battalion. Upon the arrival of Engine 61, Lieutenant Pat Durkin requested a still and box alarm. The structure involved was a three-story brick occupied, with six rental units.

Chief Hanlon related that fire was issuing from windows on both the second and third floors of the structure, and he requested a 2-11 alarm fire. The firefighters led out through the front door and Truck 30 began opening the roof until a large amount of smoke and fire caused the roof to fall inward. At this time, a 3-11 alarm was requested. At one time during the fire, three master streams and five hand lines were directed at the burning building. What once was a three-story structure had now collapsed into the first floor. We were in for a long and cold day as the temperature was twenty-two degrees and the wind was out of the north at fourteen miles per hour.

Two children were injured and taken to Billings Hospital by Ambulance 36. The Chicago police had taken a man into custody for starting this fire on the inside stairwell. He was kicked out by his girlfriend last night.

The fire had virtually annihilated the second and third floors of the subject structure. Fire destroys people and their dreams, and more importantly, causes immeasurable grief and suffering. I talked to my very old friend, Pat Durkin. He was the lieutenant of Engine Company 61 and had been for years.

Pat is not much for talking, but he told me that this fire was just a big mistake because of the man's argument with his girlfriend. "Come on," Pat said. Few sights are more impressive for their utter devastation than a building that collapsed during a fire, and Pat walked away. Bomb and Arson detectives had a confession from the suspect by the time I got to the police station. It was my second fire for the day-I hadn't even had a chance to make my bunk and it was 1800.

I don't know how many more of these winters I can take. I am cold, achy and stiff, and my neck and back are burning with pain.

It was time for Local 2 to begin preparing their wish list to present items to the city of Chicago as they begin negotiations for the next contract. Our union has sent a notification to the city for our upcoming negotiation dates. One of the major concerns that will go to the table will be the Retirees Healthcare Plan. Then we got some good news-the retro checks that we had been waiting for were coming out. The city said we would get one check now, and three more at the end of January.

I was returning from a still and box alarm in the Twenty-fourth Battalion. I heard on the radio about a still and box alarm at 72 West Fifty-fifth Street. The next thing I heard was 463 take in the still and box. I didn't think this was my fire, but the other car must be out at a fire, or committed in some way. I told Englewood Fire Alarm Office that 463 was taking in the fire on Fifty-fifth. Upon my arrival, Ambulance 36 was pulling up and firefighters were carrying out a woman who was just rescued from the fire. As paramedic Peggy Murphy ran toward the fire-fighters to assist, paramedic Eileen O'Connell released the stretcher from the ambulance and pulled it out onto the street.

An immediate assessment of the patient was being made by the paramedics, as they carefully lifted the stretcher back into the ambulance. Seconds count as these two paramedics worked on the woman and determined she had no pulse.

Eileen yells, "Let's start CPR" (cardiopulmonary resuscitation). A firefighter climbs into the ambulance. Peggy is now talking to the telemetry station. Along with me, the family members of the victim watch as the paramedics started an IV (intravenous line) into the arm of the fire victim. It was just one of those days when it took three tries to start the IV. Someone yelled "Hey, do you know what you're doing, you inconsiderate son of a bitch-that's my mother." Peggy and Eileen looked up at me and said, "Close the goddamn doors." They continued to work frantically on the woman and suddenly she began to breath. Peggy Murphy looked up and said, "Okay, we got her back" to the telemetry station. "Ambulance 36, you can transport," was the order from the telemetry hospital.

The fire was extinguished in a short time. The cause was the result of a portable electric space heater that was improperly placed too close to combustibles.

I met Ambulance 36 at the University of Chicago Hospital after the fire. I needed the name and age of the victim for my report. I told Peggy and Eileen that they did a remarkable job back there at the fire scene. As they were reorganizing their ambulance, they both said, "Yeah, yeah," and laughed it off. But I told them again what a great job they did in saving this woman's life. They just smiled and climbed back in their ambulance and returned to quarters. I know, because of my brother Mike, that when a paramedic saves a pulseless, breathless patient, no one knows the personal gratification and satisfaction a paramedic feels, knowing that this woman is still alive because they did their job. If there was any reason I would need an ambulance, I sure wanted those two paramedics to be there.

Every chance I got I studied for the upcoming examination for my Private Detective license. On a very cold morning, February 4, Engines 83 and 59, Trucks 22 and 47 and the Ninth Battalion were given a still alarm of fire to 4840 North Sheridan. Upon the arrival of Chief Schatz of the Ninth Battalion he found a very heavy smoke and fire condition in an occupied building. He requested an emergency and a still and box alarm.

Fire was issuing from a doorway in the basement in the rear of the building. As the firefighters rescued people from the building, Engines 59 and 83 led out lines in the front and back of the building. The fire escalated up through the rear wooden porches.

The temperature was a neat, clean fourteen degrees and the wind (hawk) was blowing off Lake Michigan at sixteen to twenty miles per hour. The battle continued with an inside attack. The firefighters were pushed back and the wind fueled the fire as the top floor of the structure continued to burn. I had just come around the garage on the north side of the burning structure. A firefighter was pulling on a three-inch hose, trying to get it in position. I helped him. There was just enough line to hit the fire on the third floor. I opened the nozzle on the fire and began to darken the blaze. The wind was blowing the cold water back in my face. We held on to the line. The droplets of water rolled down my neck. My body temperature seemed to go lower and lower. We shut down the big line that we were using at the rear of the building, after darkening the fire, and the firefighters made their way up the inside to the third floor. The occupants were put on a bus to keep warm. Finally, after some two hours they extinguished the fire.

The cause of this fire was an electrical malfunction in the laundry room, and I determined it to be accidental. I stayed cold for most of the day and it just made me hate Chicago's winters more and more. In six months, I would be fifty years old and retirement started looking pretty good.

After studying for the Private Detective test for so long, I felt I was prepared. I took the examination on March 15 and felt there was a good chance that I passed. In mid-March I responded to a 2-11 alarm fire in a high rise on the North Side. There were four fatalities in what ended up to be a suicide/murder fire. The news media was all over the scene trying to find out what had happened. I returned to quarters and received a call from IAD, the fire department's internal affairs office. I was told that someone had seen me take a picture frame and put it under my fire coat. I laughed when I heard this bullshit. They told me that it was not bullshit and they were going to prepare charges because it was on film.

I was pissed-off! They told me to wait in quarters until they got there with the film. We watched the film. Sure enough, I put something inside my fire coat, but it was not a picture of the people.

I explained that what I put in my fire coat was my notebook which I carry under my coat so that it will not get wet. They didn't believe me and asked me to show them. Out on the apparatus floor, I put my fire coat and truckman's belt on. I then took my notebook with brass corners on it and put it under my coat. At first they weren't too sure. I said I will bring Mr. Robert De Niro in to show you that I taught him just the same procedure while we were making the movie Backdraft. For some reason, they didn't want to challenge me anymore, and left. I guess you need those kind of people (IAD) but for me, they are a bunch of scumbags! Many times they use their authority to fuck with firefighters and paramedics.

The news traveled fast that at a 2-11 alarm fire, while pulling a line off of Engine Company 28 the engineer, Donald Kaczka, suffered a heart attack and died at the scene. The fire department prepared for another funeral and hundreds of uniformed firefighters gave a final salute to their brother and friend. Good news followed that day when I received my mail, my test scores. I had passed the examination with an 88, and that was good enough for me!

Now the summer was almost upon us, and another winter had passed. I am starting to count the working days that I have left on the job. I love being by the lake in the red and black sedan.

It brings back such good memories about the movie Backdraft. This lakefront is just magnificent. There are beaches that would make people in Florida envious. The shores are crowded with sunbathers from Hollywood Avenue on the north to the Seventy-ninth Street beaches on the south.

Yachts and sailboats glide across the water, and Grant Park is filled with people. Buckingham Fountain is my special treat every time I pass it by, especially at night when all the lights are on.

Chief Alletto told me that I would have to talk to a retirement advisor to find out about what procedure I had to do in order to retire. I called a retirement advisor named Angelo in the Kraft Building, and he informed me what to do about turning in my badge thirty days before. My father's badge 1825 was mine for almost twenty-eight years, and now it would go back into circulation on the Chicago Fire Department. It seemed like yesterday that I got that badge. Time marches on, and waits for no one!

June 15, 1995 was a nice and clear, warm day when I arrived at the firehouse. Just ten more working days left until my fiftieth birthday. Lt. Sobieski called me to the side. He said, "Hey Cos, the cook firefighter, Louie Bertnie, wants to have a cake and coffee for your last day on the job." I was taken back by the thought that they wanted to have this for me. The lieutenant was a new man in OFI, John Escamilla, and he was having a hard time adjusting to OFI, just like everyone else who started.

John told me that Bobby Villanueva's father had gotten sick in Mexico on vacation. Bobby asked me if we could be partners today, because he was going to have to pick his father up from the airport at 1400. I told Bobby no problem, if it was all right with the lieutenant.

John said he received a call from Pat Burns who said that it was okay for Bobby to pick up his sick father. We put our gear into the red and black sedan and told John we would take the first run. At 0920, Engine Company 16 was given a still alarm of fire at 4415 South Federal, the Robert Taylor Projects. Upon their arrival on the scene, heavy smoke was billowing from the windows on the east side of the structure on the fourth floor.

Engine Company 16 requested an emergency and a still and box alarm. "Four-six-four is responding to the box," Bobby said to the Main Fire Alarm Office. We were getting fuel at police headquarters at 1100 South State Street and were on the scene in minutes. There were two children in critical condition and two children in fair condition. Ambulance 35 transported the two that were critical to Michael Reese Hospital. Commissioner Orozco and Chief Alletto were on the scene. The fire was contained to apartment 401, and Engine 16 had most of the fire knocked down by the time I arrived on the floor.

The fire had originated in a bedroom and the bed was totally consumed. Back outside in the hallway I talked to a woman who was the aunt of one of the injured children. I asked her if she knew what had happened. In a crying voice, she said it was one of the boys. I ran back down the stairs to ambulance 19 and there were people all around the ambulance.

I asked if I could talk to the little boy. A Chicago police officer was trying to get some information from the young boy and said, "Good luck, he wouldn't tell me anything." I crawled into the ambulance. The paramedics were treating his burns. I explained to the paramedic Chuck Peters that I wanted to take a minute with the child. "Sure, Cos, Chuck said, "but we have to transport him now!" I removed my fire helmet and set it down next to the boy. I asked him what his name was. He was crying and was afraid of all of the people. I asked for some quiet and to close the doors of the ambulance.

Again I asked him his name as I handed him my speaker from my portable fire radio. "William," he said, crying. I assured him that everything was okay and this was an accident. I asked him if he saw the fire and he replied yes. "Where did you see the fire?" I asked him. "On the bed," he replied. "Do you know how the fire started?" and he started to cry. "No, no," I said. "It's all right. Nothing is going to happen, William," I explained. Again I asked him if he knew how the fire started. He shook his head yes. I said, "Was it a lighter or matches?" In a crying voice he said, "It was a blue lighter." Again I assured him that everything would be all right and looked at his little hands and the front of his legs. They were blistering and had burns. I looked over at Chuck Peters and said, "Take good care of William." Chuck gave me a nod and a smile and I backed out of the ambulance.

I spoke to Commissioner Orozco and Chief Alletto about the boy. Chief Alletto said, "Nice work, Cos." Commissioner Orozco asked how many days left for me, and I replied, "Just ten days to go, sir." I returned with Bobby Villanueva to the fire floor, and we finished our investigation. Chief Alletto said, "How about getting lunch?" I explained the situation with Bobby's father to Alletto. He understood and suggested I drop Bobby off at the firehouse and meet him on Taylor Street for lunch.

Back at Engine 44's quarters, I needed to exchange the battery on the portable radio. Bobby removed his gear from the car. Lieutenant John Escamilla was typing his report and informed us that he had two more reports to finish. I let him know that I would be listening to the radio, and told him to just call if he needed help.

Just at that time our speaker crackled. A still and box alarm at 2612 West Augusta, and they needed an OFI car. John Escamilla said, "Shit, I will never finish my reports." Bobby felt bad. I said, "I will take the fire in, and Bobby, you take care of the paperwork for this fire, with the kids playing with a lighter. John Escamilla said, "Thanks, Cos, I owe you one."

Upon the arrival of Engine Company 57, Captain Dick Snyder requested a still and box alarm. Battalion Six Chief Noy reported heavy smoke and fire condition in the rear of the structure. I arrived at the scene of the fire at 1200 and reported to Chief Murphy, who informed me that fire was issuing from the rear porches. I said to Chief Murphy, "I will take a look and report back to you in a little while." The firefighters were hitting the fire in the rear with two-and-a-half-inch hose lines. I went up to the floor to investigate what was burning. The kitchen and bedroom off the rear wooden porches were still burning. Firefighters were pulling the ceiling and side walls with pike poles and their axes.

Captain Dick Snyder of Engine Company 57 informed me that this was the third fire in two days with the back porches burning out of control upon their arrival. They utilized their deck gun mounted on top of the engine to extinguish most of the fire.

I told Chief Murphy what Captain Snyder had explained to me about all the fires. Mike Murphy said, "Call me later about what you found." The burn patterns under the second-floor wooden porch were indicative of a flammable/combustible liquid that had seeped through the wood. I returned to the front to tell the police officer that I was almost sure I would need to call the Bomb and Arson detectives. This was arson, and I explained the appearance of the liquid burn patterns to him.

I met Chief Noy and explained to him that I was calling the Chicago Police Bomb and Arson section. Chief Noy said, "Cos, this lady told me her son was playing with matches in the bedroom of the third floor."

"Fire burns up and out, Chief, not down, so how did the second-floor rear porches burn if the fire originated on the third floor?"

The fire companies were rolling their lines up in the rear and I told Chief Noy that I was calling for 492, the fire department's photo unit.

"Hell, Cos, I can't wait for them, I have not finished my rounds to all the firehouses."

"That's all right, Chief I will call you later, and tell you what the cause of the fire was."

I thanked Captain Snyder for the information and told him about the burn patterns on the flooring of the second-floor porch. Engine 57 was taking their one-and-three-fourth-inch hose lines down.

I reentered the burned-out structure, and went up to the second floor. In one of the rooms, a male Hispanic was going through some dresser drawers in a bedroom. I asked him what he was doing in the building. He told me that this was his apartment but I told him he couldn't be in there because we hadn't completed the investigation. He gave me some excuse and I again told him to leave the building. I was in the kitchen when he started walking out the front. I continued out onto the second-floor rear porch. The fire had burned the third-floor porches and they collapsed down onto the second floor.

I started pushing the large wooden members off the deck of the porch when all of a sudden someone grabbed my shoulder and startled me. As I turned to look who this was, my right foot went off the side of the decking of the second-floor porch. I fell about ten feet onto the stairs and then rolled the rest of the way down to a landing where my right leg went through the railing.

At first I was angry, and then came the pain. I could not move. This man came down to help me, and I told him to get help. I was lying on my back with my radio under me and my fire helmet had fallen to the ground where Engine 57 was picking up their hose. In a minute, Captain Snyder and Firefighters Louis Valadez and Patrick Ponti were at my side. They knew I was hurt and Ambulance 44 handed them the backboard.

Carefully they slid it under me, and said, "Don't worry, Cos, we got you now." Firefighter Ponti and Captain Snyder ever so carefully carried me down to Ambulance 44.

Two very special paramedics, Anna Rosa and Scott Ronstadt, transported me to Northwestern Memorial Hospital's emergency room. The doctors and nurses started to work on me and in a little while, Commissioner Orozco and Alletto were at my side, to assure me that everything would be all right. After a very thorough examination and X-rays, I was admitted to the hospital and taken to the Spinal Cord Unit.

Suzi and four of my children were with me at my bed side. I had pain everywhere in my body, but the worst pain was in my back. Into the room walked Dr. Paul Meyer, and if looks could kill, I would have been dead right there.

Dr. Meyer didn't have much to say to me, but explained to Suzi that I had struck my mid-thoracic and right scapular area. He further said that in the X-rays, the fusion and the instrumentation in my back did not appear to have any disruption. "There is a lot of pain in the right side of his back, and so I have decided to proceed with surgery to remove all the hardware of longitudinal rods, and the cross members." The surgery took about four and a half hours.

After the surgery, I had to see Dr. Meyer and he still seemed to be a little angry with me. He said, "Don't even ask the question about going back on the Chicago Fire Department."

I was privileged to work as a Chicago firefighter, and I will always be proud of that fact. It was going to be very difficult for me to reconcile myself to the fact that it was over for me. When faced with forced retirement, one where you have no choice about the decision, it is tough to handle, and very depressing.

Epiloque

The Chicago Fire Department has always had to make changes, and it is no different today than it was years ago. Many of these changes are derived from experiences and situations that have occurred over the years.

The Chicago fire of 1871, when 300 people were lost and 18,000 buildings went up in flames, caused changes to be made, and the fire department expanded rapidly. The horse-drawn steam engines were the pride of the fire department and in 1923, Engine 11 made its last horse-drawn run.

The first automobiles replaced the chief's buggies, then the engine companies changed from all horses to all motors. In the 1930s, there were more changes, engine's hose beds were now one-and-a-half-inch and three-inch hose beds. Modern sedan pumpers with cabs were purchased. World War II drained the fire department of manpower, and after the war a firefighter from Truck Company 11 started the ambulance service in the Chicago Fire Department.

In 1957, big changes were made when Robert J. Quinn became the fire commissioner. The apparatus called the snorkel was unveiled and proved to be very successful at fighting fires. Chiefs were given station wagons and were given ambulance calls. Helicopters and sea rescue boats were now added to the department.

In 1961, the old drill school was replaced by a new modern fire academy, where most of this fire department today received their training. In the 1970s, the fire department enlarged the ambulance service to forty-three ambulances, with both male and female paramedics. Chicago's firefighters were confronted with the coldest, snowiest winters in history.

In 1980, the first firefighter's strike brought on unprecedented changes after a bitter twenty-three days of conflict and won the first firefighter contract. The department was restructured from seven divisions into six districts. In 1982, a big change in communications was made when all fire companies were issued portable radios.

In 1988, the Chicago Fire Department began sending engine and truck companies to emergency medical service (EMS) calls. This was called the first responder.

As fire calls decreased and ambulance calls increased, the fire department started training firefighters in the basic and advanced life support techniques. Most of the training consisted of cardiopulmonary resuscitation (CPR) and basic first aid.

There is no way around this demand for EMS. Some firefighters say they just get more ambulances, but that's like putting a Band-Aid on a tumor. To avoid a massive increase in ambulance calls, the department added twenty-seven advanced life support (ALS) engine companies to the fifty-nine ALS ambulances now on the department. Also, the fire department has added twelve BLS (basic life support) ambulances staffed by firefighter/EMTs (emergency medical technicians).

The increase in EMS calls, not only in Chicago, but all over America is remarkable, and at times is overwhelming. Especially during the hot summer months. This ambulance work is not new to the firefighters, because in the old days we had a pulmotor that responded to EMS calls, administering oxygen to the victims, and in some cases transporting them to a nearby hospital.

The fire department has taken a big turn in the last few years, with a 20 percent drop in fires, and a major increase in EMS calls. With the cross-training of firefighters and paramedics, along with the haz-mat emergencies, fires, and many other tasks, the department thinks it will have a more rounded person to respond and protect the citizens of Chicago.

Regardless of all the changing times, the fire service is still the same. They call, and we respond. The pride of this job is to belong to a firehouse, a company. Whether it is an engine, truck, or an ambulance, the pride of being on the Chicago Fire Department is still there.

Most of the firefighters I knew were thrilled to be on this job. Much of their pride was built around the notion that they did a job most others were afraid to attempt.

Today, when a few of our brothers or sisters make a mistake, or get into some type of trouble, we hear about it "big time," through the newspapers, television, and radio. But, when they make a lifesaving rescue there are only tidbits in the news about the incident.

A very few make "race" an issue, but in most cases race has nothing to do with it-most of the time it's just personalities. In most firehouses, African American and Caucasian firefighters get along and work well together. The news media would have citizens thinking that white firefighters and paramedics sit in a corner, and the African American firefighters sit in another corner, and that's just not true.

We have about 5,000 firefighters and paramedics on this job, and when you have that many people, things do occur. But in any industry with that many people working, personalities will clash. I have said this before, and I will say it again, the kitchen is the "hub of the firehouse" and the cooking club establishes harmony to all!

The platoon with discipline and a sincere interest in the job will find cooperation and enjoyment of their work among its members. A well-disciplined, well-trained company justifies its existence by its performance, both in and out of quarters. The stories in this book are about the firefighters and paramedics who risk their lives to save another.

It doesn't make a difference if it is the poorest citizen in a rat-infested tenement building, because to firefighters and paramedics they have as high a value as the occupant of a high-rise building on Chicago's Gold Coast.

Like always, firefighters perform the gruesome task of removing victims from the twisted wreckage of train crashes, motor vehicle crashes, and airplane crashes. When you turn on your television news at the end of your day, the scene is always the same. The first thing you see is firefighters with their reflective fire coats and that odd-shaped helmet on their heads, climbing into or onto the wreckage of some crash. You see paramedics ever so carefully placing victims on stretchers, administering oxygen and starting life saving techniques.

Time and time again, the most astonishing thing about firefighters is their ability to do things that some people say was humanly impossible.

Remember, for over 150 years firefighters have been America's domestic defenders. They have been out there, not just responding to fires, but to every type of disaster, man-made and natural, that occurs. Whether it is a hurricane, an earthquake, a flood, a tornado, or a fire, firefighters are out there helping the citizens of this country.

Firefighting has become increasingly complex and dangerous. Despite constant improvements to protective clothing and equipment, and despite the strengthening of health and safety regulations, firefighting still remains a very dangerous profession. I am not sure if you know this, but two out of every five firefighters are injured in the line of duty.

Then there are times when firefighters and paramedics make the ultimate sacrifice, and give their lives in the line of duty. Oftentimes, when a tragic death occurs to a firefighter, he or she is noted as a hero. But the death didn't make them heroes, what they did while in the course of their careers made them heroes, because they were firefighters.

Firefighters are not strangers to death, but when a tragic death occurs to a firefighter, a brother whom we all worked with, the hurt and pain is passed down to their families and friends. The spouses and families mourn their losses for years, and children of fallen firefighters suffer lasting scars and injuries. A perfect example was the recent untimely deaths of Lieutenant L. C. Merrill and Lieutenant Scott Gillen.

I included this epilogue so that young firefighters and paramedics who will follow on this job, will have a better idea of what it means to be part of this noble profession.

A Prayer for Firemen

When they are called to duty, God
Whenever flames may rage
Give them the strength to save
some life, Whatever be its age,
Help them embrace a little child
Before it is too late,
Or save an older person
From the horror of that fate
Enable them to be alert
And hear the weakest shout
And quickly and efficiently
To put the fire out
And if according to Your will
They have to lose their lives
Please bless with Your hand
Their children and their wives.

STOCKYARDS FIRE MEMORIAL

The Chicago Stockyards Fire Memorial

Remembering the Fallen 21

On December 22, 1910, a collapsing wall killed twenty-one
Chicago firefighters combatting a blaze in the historic
Stockyards District.

The Chicago Stockyards Fire Memorial Fund,
a non-profit organization, has selected Chicago artist Tom Scarff
to create a sculpture honoring the Fallen 21 in a public
monument befitting their sacrifice.

Scheduled for completion in late 2002, the 18 ft. high bronze
and aluminum sculpture will be set in a landscaped
meditation garden. Backed by a "Wall of Honor" with the names
of all Chicago Fire Department firefighters and paramedics
who have given their lives in the line of duty,
the Chicago Stockyards Fire Memorial will be a tribute
to the Fallen 21 and all those who served and
died in defense of this great city.

To help make this vision a reality, please send your contribution to:

The Chicago Stockyards Fire Memorial Fund
c/o Lerner & Wilhoite
117 North Jefferson Street
Suite 301
Chicago, IL 60661*

thank you for helping us
Remember the Fallen 21 & all Firefighters
who have given the supreme sacrifice.

*Your contribution is tax-deductible to the extent that the law allows.

In memory of the New York Firefighters and paramedics who made the ultimate sacrifice for their fellow human beings.

September 11, 2001

I mourn with you

The choice is not ours, it is true!

But, if you think it over a bit, we've come to the conclusion that the best possible circumstance for their death as firefighters is that they were doing what they were trained to do, and loved doing,

"Being Firefighters"

Especially if the work involves doing something for our fellow human beings.

— Rev Father Mathew McDonald
Retired Chicago Fire Department Chaplain

In memory of the fallen New York Firefighters, and
paramedics who made the ultimate sacrifice for their
fellow human beings.

September 11, 2001

I MOURN WITH YOU